Crying and Res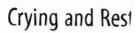

Ria Blom

Crying and Restlessness in Babies

A Parent's Guide to Natural Sleeping

Floris Books

Translated by George Hall and Liesbeth Machielsen

First published in Dutch in 2003 as *Regelmaat en inbakeren —*
Voorkomen én verhelpen van huilen en onrust
by Uitgevereij Christofoor, Zeist
First published in English in 2005 by Floris Books, Edinburgh

British Library CIP Data available

ISBN 0-86315-491-3

Produced in Poland by Polskabook

Foreword

Some babies drive their parents mad with their crying and restlessness. Moreover, they keep themselves awake and thus suffer from a shortage of sleep. Such babies need regularity and uniformity.

A lack of sleep, which afflicts both babies and parents, is a breeding ground for uncertainty, doubt, feelings of failure, gloominess and even depression. A baby's crying evokes physiological reactions from everyone: disquiet and stress, certainly if the crying never seems to stop.

Immediately after birth, security, tenderness and love are of the essence. The first year of life is the most important period for the development of a new human being. Three months of crying can be classified as a 'poor start:' the sunny skies become cloudy, the rainclouds gather grey and sombre, and tears fall.

This book offers clarity, is written in a brisk style, and parents' narratives are recognizable, especially to those with a crying and restless child. Young parents who look forward to happy times with their adorable and good-humoured baby, refreshed from sleep, will benefit from reading this book. Grandparents will nod in agreement. They understand why their approach worked so well in their time, because this book explains the active elements of their approach to their own children. Present-day parents are different: they first want to know and understand, and only then do they begin to apply any advice. This pioneering book on rest, rhythm and regulation is ideal for them.

The first part outlines the theory of the young child's development and the importance of rhythm, predictability and love. The second part explains the approach in detail, so that the reader can readily deploy it.

Predictable regulation does not mean 'rigid and unwa-
vering.' It is merely the natural balance between sleeping,
eating, cuddling, playing alone and falling asleep again.

More than a fifth of the children in the world are swaddled.
It is an ancient custom, now presented in a new style. The
extent to which swaddling, when applied in combination
with rhythm and regulation, has more value than rhythm
and regulation alone is currently the topic of scientific
research. The theory arising on this subject — the regulation of young children which is so necessary right from
the outset and which is excellently described by the author
— should see the light of day as soon as possible. Many
parents will benefit greatly from this.

Dr M.P. L'Hoir
Psychotherapist, the Wilhelmina Child Hospital / University
Hospital, Utrecht

Utrecht, Spring 2003

Preface

Most of the experiences recounted in this book were written by parents, who all gave their permission for publication. Nevertheless, the names of those concerned have been changed to guarantee their privacy.

The information and advice provided in this book has been assessed by various professional colleagues. However, this book must not be regarded as a replacement for medical professionals. It serves as additional support. All the themes that are discussed in this book are also topics for discussion with the above professionals, so do not hesitate to put your questions to him or her.

Whatever the case, you should consult a medical practitioner if you want to swaddle your child. A doctor or nurse can check whether or not swaddling is the appropriate action in your situation. An examination can be performed as to whether or not there are any contraindications, in other words, if there are medical reasons why your child should not be swaddled. If the child is swaddled, a nurse may provide welcome assistance.

Not being in a position to supervise your actions, the author of this book cannot accept any responsibility concerning the way in which you apply regularity and swaddling.

Introduction

This book deals with the swaddling of babies, but not exclusively. It also covers how you can avoid the necessity of swaddling. The basic principles that are necessary to break the cycle of increasing restlessness and crying are the same as those that can prevent the occurrence of this cycle. Prevention being better than cure, the basic principles and corresponding insights will be first explained. Then the book will deal with swaddling itself, which is a temporary measure. It will become clear that the measures that generate rhythm and uniformity can be maintained when peace and quiet have returned, right up to the age of eighteen years, albeit in a different form, suitable for the child's age.

The book consists of two parts. Part I explores the causes of crying and restlessness.

First there is an investigation into why so many children these days sleep so little, cry so much, whine and are so restless. Furthermore, it provides insight into development and upbringing, so that a negative cycle of crying and restlessness can be prevented.

The following themes are dealt with in this part:

✿ trends in upbringing over the last few decades
✿ the developmental phases of the infant, with corresponding pitfalls and advice on how to avoid these
✿ the importance of healthy sensory development and the significance of sleep
✿ the link between routine and the quality of sleeping and drinking patterns
✿ from crying and comforting to habituation and pampering

Part 2 deals with solving crying and restlessness. This part describes two methods to reverse the pattern of excessive crying and restlessness. These two methods are:

✿ the application of predictable regularity and uniformity without swaddling
✿ the application of predictable regularity and uniformity with swaddling

How it all began

I started using swaddling in 1994. Why did I choose this approach? I had observed that children were becoming increasingly restless. Three weeks after the birth of a baby, a whole family might be completely adrift due to fatigue. I found that rather unsettling. After all, every birth is an exceptional event, the beginning of a lengthy growth process supervised by the parents. A basic ambience of happiness, peace and trust should prevail.

It was the beginning of my search for a solution. In addition to increasing restlessness, I also noticed an absence of routine that led to a loss of sleep. This was not because babies needed less sleep but because, unnoticed, they were kept in their mother's or father's arms more, and for longer periods. Due to the attention they received, they seemed alert and awake, so that any underlying tiredness was camouflaged. Their apparent alertness invited parents to pay even more attention to the children. Finally, the children became dependent on this attention. Parents told me that their children could not be alone. After a maximum of five minutes in the playpen, they wanted to be lifted up again, and once back in their mother's arms, they were happy and content. At bedtime, the children would not go to sleep.

Instead of allowing themselves to be put down to sleep, the children began to cry the moment they touched the mattress. And if they were asleep when they were put to bed, they awoke too early. These children had frequent catnaps and often asked to be fed. Their tiredness then prevented them from consuming the whole feed, they often fell asleep during the breast or bottle-feeding, were put to bed and woke up crying half an hour later. When they were lifted up, they emitted a hearty laugh, which usually meant that 'the sleep was over.'

I not only observed this increasing restlessness, but also the way the children were put down to sleep. This seemed to have changed in the course of time. This same group of children had a lot of 'freedom' in bed, as the blankets were hardly tucked in and did not extend much further than the children's chest. The arms and hands, which remained uncovered, were often cold. Parents told me that there was nothing wrong with this. I also saw many children clothed in thin cotton, regardless of which season it was. I never saw a sleeping bag or a shawl with these children. They seemed to grow slowly and did not seem to be thriving; their eyes were gaunt and they occasionally had a worried frown on their foreheads. Their arms were usually a blur of movement over which they had little control — there appeared to be no *pleasure* in the movement. The parents did not know when they had to be ready for their child because there was no routine. If it was not their first child, the situation was soon acute. Parents have more time for their first child, and I saw many parents who, with the best intentions, completely sacrificed themselves. This surplus of benevolence concealed their own fatigue for a long time, but sooner or later the flexibility wore off. Little remained of the pleasure and genuine contact with their child. Among this group, I observed a great deal of uncertainty with regard to the child's upbringing.

In contrast to this group of children and their parents, I saw a group of children who, for the first six months of their lives, seemed to be perfectly capable of amusing themselves in the playpen after feeding and then slept for two hours until the next feed. They drank heartily and lay satisfied in their parents' arms in the afterglow of their meal. In addition to being together, it was self-evident that these children could be alone and play by themselves. And when they indicated that they were tired, they were put to bed to sleep until hunger woke them again. Then it was feeding time again. This group of children was clothed and covered up in bed in such a way that they could retain sufficient body heat and had fewer problems with cold hands and feet. I did not always see a sleeping bag or a shawl, but tight blankets had a similar function. The shawl was mainly used to enclose the child when he or she woke up. The change in temperature between the bed and the changing or feeding place was thus minor. This group of children cried a lot less and was clearly more satisfied. They truly enjoyed moving their arms and legs of their own accord. They were their own boss. Their growth rates were average to above average. In short, these children thrived on all fronts. There was predictable routine in their lives and in the lives of their parents. This ensured that everyone knew what could be expected. There was alternation of care provision and free time. All members of the family benefited from this, and there was little uncertainty about the child's upbringing.

By comparing these two groups of children, the differences furnished me with an indication of where to look for a possible answer to my question:

*For which reasons can the basic feeling of joy and confidence
be so easily lost and how can this feeling be restored?*

The differences can be denoted by the following keywords:

- ✿ RHYTHM versus an *absence of rhythm*
- ✿ SELF-RELIANCE versus *having to be entertained*
- ✿ FALLING ASLEEP OF ONE'S OWN ACCORD versus *being
  lulled to sleep*
- ✿ LENGTHY SLEEP versus *catnaps*
- ✿ WARMTH versus *cold*

During my consultancy, I became acquainted with swaddling via a Dutch mother and her Bolivian partner. They
swaddled their daughter, Mirza, according to the Bolivian
tradition. As a result, her restlessness, frequent urge to
drink and scanty periods of sleep became things of the past.
Could swaddling thus be an answer to the trends that were
becoming apparent in the Netherlands? I was impressed by
the narrative of Marianne, the mother, and the contented-
ness that her daughter radiated. Swaddling was one step
further than the use of the wrap-around leg blanket and the
body shawl itself, with which I was familiar.

With a certain amount of hesitation, I began to apply it
as a method. It was new to me, although the technique itself
was as old as Methuselah. I wondered whether or not it was
suitable for the present day. Was I capable of explaining the
underlying reason for this course of action to parents? I had
to make some kind of conversion to modern times — adopt-
ing something from a different culture or from a bygone
age doesn't usually work.

To me, it became a voyage of discovery lasting years.
Devoting attention to observing and listening was a precondition: observing the child and listening to the parents

before deciding whether or not to swaddle the child. And during the swaddling process it was also essential to continue my observations, and to adjust the process where necessary.

Certain patterns began to become obvious and it became increasingly clear when swaddling was or was not the appropriate method. After extensive discussions about two swaddled children with the team of therapists with whom I work, the pieces of the puzzle finally fell into place. Finally, in 1994, the concise brochure, *The Child Wrapped in Swaddling Clothes,* appeared. This brochure contains a photographic session on swaddling, with Mirza as an example, and provides an outline of the method, written by her mother Marianne de Jong. The many experiences, discussions with colleagues and literature study made it necessary to rewrite the brochure a few years later (April 2001). The swaddling method had also changed. This was adjusted to the prevailing insights at that time and was adapted to accommodate the experiences with swaddling that we had gained. The new book had the title *Inbakkeren brengt rust* (Swaddling Brings Rest). The contents of that book, which is still available in print, are fully interwoven with the text of this book.

Please note: for reasons of conciseness, I use the term 'he' to refer to babies of either gender.

Part 1

Causes of Crying and Restlessness

1. Upbringing

Trends of upbringing over the past few decades

Various upbringing trends have become evident in the past few decades. In the forties and fifties, the terms Rest, Rhythm and Hygiene were the great mainstays. There was a tradition that was passed on from mother to daughter. One did everything exactly as it should be and gave it no more thought. One was busy primarily with everyday worries, such as earning one's daily bread. Moreover, looking after large families demanded a great deal of time and effort. There were no washing machines in those days. The children had little deliberate influence on family affairs. Unruly children were disciplined by the father, and once that had happened, the children again knew their place.

In the sixties and seventies, the style of upbringing swung dramatically the other way. There was much more prosperity, the crisis of the war years had been left behind and there was employment for everyone. Young people threw off the straitjacket of many established traditions. It was the time of *Flower Power* and increasing individual freedom. Everyone could take part in any discussion. Old values and norms were cast overboard. It was a time of *anti-authoritarian* upbringing. Children were no longer regarded as inferior but were put on an equal footing with adults, regardless of how small they might be. The word 'authority' disappeared into the background. Parents regarded their children as friends rather than their inferiors. Rules and regulations relaxed. The pram was gradually replaced by the sling, the pouch on the parent's body. The child no longer had to sleep in its cot but was taken along everywhere. Upbringing was no longer solely the duty of the mother. The increased use of bottle-feeding allowed the father to 'mother' the child as well. Breast-feeding was on demand rather than according to a schedule. Day nurseries appeared allowing mothers to go to work, based on the idea that it was good for their social development if infants were used to being with other infants. It was also the era of a *laissez-faire* upbringing, akin to an anti-authoritarian upbringing but less outspoken. 'Let it be,' everything is allowed. Limits blurred and there were few imperatives or prohibitions. The child was given every freedom to indulge itself. The mainstays of upbringing — Rest, Rhythm and Hygiene — were washed away. Of course, not everyone adhered to this *laissez-faire* and anti-authoritarian approach. Many adopted a middle course. In the meantime, it became increasingly difficult to raise a child with the family as model and support. Individualization loosened the family links and family members lived increasingly far from one another.

Parenthood nowadays

Now that we have entered the 21st century, we see that both methods of upbringing are outdated. We have discovered that upbringing without limits has its darker side. Primary schools in particular are having to bear the brunt of this.

Nowadays, upbringing has become an issue of applying one's own ideas rather than deploying traditional methods. We do our own thing, try to do our best, and want to do it differently from our parents. However, most parents are still inexperienced when their first-born arrives. Popular magazines on parenting sell well, just as books on parenting do. This flood of information makes it difficult to see the wood for the trees. A modern man or woman is also much more of a 'head' person — in other words, is more engaged in thinking — so that it has become more difficult to act intuitively, or with some kind of natural knowledge. Accordingly, it is no surprise that developments from the *negotiation model* are applied in upbringing. Children are regarded as equal discussion partners. You can tell children the truth, even if they are very small. One does not need to repeat the story of the stork or the cabbage patch if a three year old asks where children come from. Children are entitled to an honest answer. We no longer need to conceal or envelop things in a fairytale. We respect the choice of a two year old. If he indicates that he no longer wants to have an afternoon nap, that is accepted. We communicate on an 'adult-level' with three year olds. The 'why' question sessions are answered as faithfully as possible. Children are not only seen as being equal on a verbal level, but also on an emotional level. A child's expression of feelings is interpreted according to adult standards. Crying is sometimes erroneously explained as an expression of grief or of loneliness. Based on this interpretation, the only response is to pick the child up and comfort it.

The present-day consumer society with its 24/7 economy does not make it any easier for the upbringer. As a result, the routine that is so beneficial in a child's life is sometimes completely lacking. Increasing individualization has made raising children a real art. It is certainly not easy for new parents to discover what their child really needs. Our senses are inundated with information but we generally do not notice this because we are so used to it. As a result, we do not take a moment to consider that children *can* be overwhelmed and overstimulated.

2. Developmental phases and pitfalls in the first three years of life

Insight into child development, with its corresponding changes in behaviour, can help solve the 'problems' that arise. Without insight, this changing behaviour may represent a pitfall. Before you know it, habits that you would prefer not to appear, have established themselves clandestinely. Bad habits are easily learned but are difficult to unlearn. It is better to prevent the forming of unwanted habits. This theme deserves much attention.

The birth of a child changes your life completely. A new balance is hesitatingly sought, and can easily be shattered again in the first three years of life. A new stage of development, with corresponding new behaviour that you do not understand, can be the cause of this. These developmental changes follow one another in rapid succession in the first three years of life. Just when you think you have reached calm water, the next change arrives. You can feel like you are continually fire-fighting, with all possible consequences: more whining and crying, a decrease in the child's capacity to be alone and amuse himself, and an increasingly chaotic pattern of sleeping and feeding.

The stage from newborn to six weeks old is given extra attention because this is where the foundation is laid for upbringing and development. Experience shows that the origins of the problems of restlessness and excessive crying usually lie in the first or second week of life.

Newborns up to six weeks old

The newly-born child finds itself between heaven and earth, as it were. Most of the time is devoted to sleeping or eating. After feeding, the baby usually falls asleep in its mother's arms and can then be laid quietly in its cot. The first experiences with this world mainly occur via skin contact. From birth, the baby's arms in particular are constantly moving and the first 'smiles' soon appear. It simply happens at random.

> 'After birth, the baby will never feel quite as safe and sound as it felt in the womb. The pleasant warmth and the feeling of being limited by the mother's body suddenly vanish. Instead the child will experience cold, hunger and when he moves his arms he will feel unlimited space. For this reason, you should keep the world small in the first few weeks after birth.
>
> You will recover more quickly if you give yourself the opportunity to get used to the new rhythm with your baby. Put the brake on too many maternal visits and don't let your child be passed around as this can be rather unsettling. Protect your child from unnecessary stimuli.'[1]

In the first six weeks of life, toys are completely superfluous, regardless of how cosy or charming a row of teddy bears may be. A small cuddly toy in the cradle is sufficient. Ignore the baby-gym and cassette tapes for the first three months. Your child will not benefit from these even if they seem to help. In fact, a child of this age will soon devote his full attention to the baby-gym or the mobile that you constantly set in motion; he cannot ignore these and will soon suffer from overstimulation.

Warmth

A baby who is nice and warm feels comfortable and secure. The warmth with which you literally, and figuratively, wrap him up ensures that he can grow and develop. It is important to enjoy equal warmth, including warm hands and feet in bed. Of course, being too warm is not good. If a child is not uniformly warm, he will feel uncomfortable and can become restless or even suffer from stomach cramps.[2]

Clothing

In the first few weeks, a small cap made of silk, soft wool or cotton (depending on the season) will keep your baby's head nice and warm. This is important because at this stage, the head represents a quarter of the entire body. Leave the forehead open so that the child can lose any excess warmth. If you swaddle your child, a cap should *not* be used.

Make sure you use warm clothes, preferably made of natural material, which retain body warmth and expel any excess warmth. There are woollen or woollen/silk tricot vests and nappy vests that feel just as thin and supple as cotton vests. The insulating property of clothing depends on the amount of air that is trapped between the various layers. Woollen clothes contain more air than cotton ones. If you are using cotton, always give your child two layers of long sleeves, extending right down to the hands, so that the body warmth can be retained better by the insulating effect of the intermediary air. Then the hands, which are usually outside the blankets, will become less cold. For children who quickly throw off their blankets, or who tend to be cold by nature, the old-fashioned sleeve-vest is ideal.

The sleeve-vest

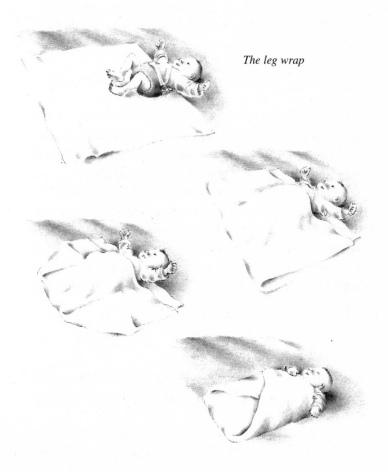

The leg wrap

The leg wrap

Instead of a sleepsuit (footie) or pants (trousers), the more practical leg wrap can be used in the first six weeks (see illustration p. 25). The lower part of the body feels nice and warm and the child feels his own legs and feet and the limits of the wrap. In contrast, if pants (trousers) are used, the lower legs are often exposed, leading to loss of warmth. In addition, the limitation of the leg wrap tends to have a calming influence. The wrap should be loose enough for the child to spread his legs in a natural pose, so that hip development is not impeded.

The bed

After the seclusion of the womb, the cradle is the next logical step, although a larger bed might seem more practical. The familiar seclusion can be simulated by laying the child under a well tucked-in blanket that covers the child up to his chin, perhaps in combination with an old-fashioned shawl. A bed of the appropriate size with the fixed limitations of the blankets will offer your child seclusion and help the length and the quality of his sleep. Waving the arms due to reflexes or cramps is restrained in such a way that sleep is barely disturbed. (For a detailed description of the ideal bed, see Chapter 12)

Room temperature

Rather than increase room temperature, you should clothe your child and tuck him in so that he can retain his own body warmth.

Adapt a newborn's clothes and blankets to a room temperature of 17–18°C. In the first few days after birth, the midwife and/or maternity nurse will advise you about the periods and the extent to which hot-water bottles are needed. If a child can keep himself warm without a hot-water bottle, a lower room temperature of 15–18°C is recommended. You will have to adapt the clothes and blankets if the weather is warmer so that your child will not become too hot. Nevertheless, even in warm weather you should cover your child with at least a sheet so that he will not lose his warmth to the air, resulting in a restless sleep.

Feeding and sleeping

With breast-feeding in particular, the first few days are dominated by starting up the feeding. It is good to pay attention to the introduction of a measure of routine in the feeding and to approach this in combination with sleeping. Once the feeding has got into full swing, after two or three days, it is advisable — even with a feeding-on-demand approach — to allow at least two hours between feeds. This is necessary to give the child and the digestive processes some rest. For your child, it is natural to feed as soon as he wakes up, and to be laid to sleep at the first signs of tiredness. Accordingly, a regular sleeping/drinking rhythm can develop, which will benefit all parties. More information on this topic is provided in Chapter 5.

Putting the child to bed

Place your child in bed before he falls asleep so that he can fall asleep himself. Of course, this does not mean that you should wake up your newborn when he falls asleep during feeding in the first few days of his life.

Some children need to cry a little before going to sleep. This should last no longer than ten minutes. You should allow the child to cry. For many children this is normal and they are not at all miserable. Trying to avoid this can lead to sleeping problems, leading to more restlessness and crying.

When your child is awake and you lay him to sleep in his bed, he will begin to recognize the bed as the sleeping place and will surrender to sleep. This recognition does not happen if your child is already asleep when you put him to bed. Putting a sleeping child to bed after a small feed from the breast or bottle might seem ideal. In the first two or three weeks of life a newborn will easily sleep for two hours at a stretch. However, if the parents adhere to this habit, a change soon occurs. Many children begin to sleep for shorter periods or even tend to wake up as soon as they touch the mattress. One can only guess as to the reasons for this. I suspect that the child subconsciously feels that he is no longer in the arms of his parents. The older the child, the more quickly he observes this. Due to ignorance about the amount of sleep the child generally needs, a shorter sleep (from half an hour to an hour) is soon accepted on the basis of the idea that 'my child apparently needs less sleep now that he is older.'

Putting your child to bed when he is asleep, then, has consequences in the long run. If you do this from the beginning and continue to do so, the following routine arises:

✿ In the first one to two weeks that a sleeping child is put to bed, the child will sleep for two hours at a time.

✿ From three to six weeks old, a sleeping child that is put to bed will awake after about half an hour. He wakes up crying and does not want to be put back to bed. This is how catnaps begin.

✿ After about six weeks, the child wakes up when he feels the mattress. Bed is rejected. He then has to be lulled or rocked to sleep and again laid down — if you are lucky. If not, he will enjoy a nap on the parent's

arm. The overfatigued child will tend to sleep the
whole night — that is a matter of survival.

✿ At the age of around three months, putting the child
to bed, either sleeping or awake, will be a problem.
The child will not want to sleep during the day, but
will sleep at night.

✿ At around five months, this restlessness will also
become apparent in the night and going to sleep
in the evening becomes increasingly difficult. The
child is now strong enough to keep himself awake
in the nighttime.

Apparently a child can become accustomed to being put to
bed when it is asleep, which results in the negative consequence that he does not sleep for long enough. However, a
child ought to learn to go to bed when he is still awake and
learn to fall asleep himself. This recognition of the sleeping
place makes it a trusted environment. This trust and security ensure that the child surrenders to sleep and enjoys the
necessary amount of sleep, no more and no less. Chapter 4
deals with the importance of sleep.

Pitfall
The habit of putting a sleeping child to bed will lead to
increasingly poor sleep within 4–6 weeks.

Around six weeks

A healthy child of around six weeks old will look and
smile at you. The child is becoming visibly alert to the
world around him. Besides the basic needs for feeding and

sleeping, he will remain awake longer after every feed to look at and feel the environment that exists within his field of vision. Tender vocal noises emerge and he reacts to the voices of family members. If the child is tired, this will be clearly obvious to the carer. When the first signals of tiredness are met consistently by being put to bed, the child will accept this without resistance. Some children seem to need a cry to fall asleep. It seems that they arrive in a kind of unloved no-man's land in the transition from being awake to falling asleep. Crying may be a help in shutting himself off from his surroundings. The arms display more movement, so that it looks like they have lost all hold. The parent who has learned to accept a bout of crying will experience that the child will fall silent within a few minutes, often in the middle of a yell. He is asleep.

Experiences of touch are random. The child cannot yet deliberately touch or grab things. His skin feels where he touches something due to his own movement or where something external touches him. As the child becomes older, the movements of the arms and legs become more purposeful. The development of motor skills — 'becoming awake in one's own body' — arrives step by step, from head to toe.

Around three months

The child who was accustomed to drinking fully from the breast or bottle will now release it when the most acute hunger has been relieved in order to attract the attention of the parent with a good-humoured laugh. The child has learned that his laughing and gurgling evoke a response. He becomes inquisitive and increasingly seeks contact. The nature of the child determines the keenness with which he does so. The degree of enthusiasm that the child receives as a response will reinforce the child's eagerness to a greater or lesser extent. In the first week of this great acquisition — being able to establish deliberate contact — many children have to be assisted in focusing on the matter at hand during the feeding. You can reduce the stimuli during feeding times by temporarily feeding the child in bed, or sitting in a chair with a shawl around you in a peaceful environment without a radio or telephone. When the amiable laugh of the child is answered with a smile, it will tend to return sooner to the breast or bottle.

Pitfall

When the parent, on the basis of his or her own feelings, reacts enthusiastically toward the child, the child may tend to drink too little. When the first pangs of hunger have been relieved, the child will opt for pleasure rather than drinking, with the result that he will require feeding more often. This feeding pattern will have a negative influence on the sleeping pattern.

A three-month-old child discovers his own hands and learns to grab things deliberately. In doing so, the surrounding world becomes larger. He can deliberately push himself away from the breast or suddenly turn his head away. This may also cause a sloppy and restless feeding pattern. It also tends to make the nursing mother uncertain. She may ask herself if she is producing enough milk. A three-month-old child also learns to control his legs. The increasingly enthusiastic thrashing around, the throwing off of blankets in bed, and pushing against the edge of the playpen are all evidence of this. In a vertical position, the child will attempt to push himself upwards by thrusting out his feet. It is marvellous to see how a child, from head to toe, becomes conscious of his own body. It is no longer something that is moved by reflexes, but is now something that is set in motion by the child himself. A three-month-old child still acts primarily in a horizontal dimension. Providing him with the horizontal surface of the playpen or the floor is still preferable to a bouncing / rocker chair or first-stage car seat. Lying on a hard surface is a precondition for movement and of raising oneself up.

Up to the age of three months, the crying of a healthy baby is usually a sign of 'I'm tired or I'm hungry.' Around three months, it may begin to mean that the child is bored because the desired playthings are not available. He has now discovered that he can deliberately use his hands. He wishes to practise abundantly by reaching for, grabbing and holding everything within reach. Playthings right next to the child are often outside of his field of vision. The mobile that rotates high above him is no longer interesting. He can only look at it. The child will gain much more pleasure from more subtle playthings, hanging on a safe line within his reach or in the corner of the playpen. If these hang in a corner and not right above his face, the playthings are not forced upon the child. It is preferable to allow him to turn his head toward the place where objects are suspended.

Pitfall

Interpreting the behaviour of a child on the basis of our own thoughts can lead to the wrong conclusions such as: My child doesn't want a blanket — My child doesn't want to sleep — My child wants to sit up in his rocking seat.

Around six months

At this age, the child begins to become a world citizen. He
becomes interested in eating solid food with a spoon. This
is a matter of habituation or conditioning. Mouth movements of a completely different kind are needed — they differ greatly from those needed for drinking from the breast
or bottle. As a result, each spoonful that enters his mouth is
returned three times. The child gurgles, spatters and blows
bubbles as a reaction to the totally new feeling that a spoon
and solid food give. It does not mean that the child does not
like the food, but it is his way of exploring this new world.
It is essential that parents interpret this behaviour properly.
For the learning experience, it is necessary to continue to
offer solid food step by step. The child will soon learn what
the intention is. This process of conditioning will be more

difficult if the provision of solid food is consistently interrupted or even postponed. In this period, most children are
ready, in terms of development, for spoon-feeding. If we
skip this learning period, eating problems may arise. If a
child is only offered liquid feeds for too long, he will not
be satisfied and will whine more as a result. Without really
being noticed, night feeds may become necessary. Here
again, feeding and sleep patterns are closely linked to one
another.

Pitfall

Interpreting sputtering and returning solid food in
terms of: 'My child does not like it' or 'My child is not
ready for it' may lead to eating problems and to restless
sleep due to hunger.

Six to nine months

The child begins to display anxiety about being separated
from his parents: this is an expression of a budding capacity to distinguish. When you leave the room, your child
may suddenly begin to cry. To a child in this phase, 'out
of sight' literally means 'no longer exists.' Nevertheless,
the child has to learn that people and things do come
back. You should not try to avoid this sorrow, which is
an essential part of learning about the world. However,
you can help your child with it. For example, you can
leave the room but keep on talking or singing to your
child. A self-confident attitude helps to establish trust. Do
not give in to your child's uncertainty. If you sit at your
child's bedside until he falls asleep, the covert message

is that it is scary to fall asleep alone. This is the phase for peek-a-boo games, such as picking things from a playpen, placing a cloth over them and then removing the cover, or placing a cloth over your own head and allowing the child to pull it off. As a result, the child learns in a playful way that things that vanish from sight have not ceased to exist.

In this period, the child also begins to distinguish between known and unknown people. His worldview, in which everything was the same, now begins to change. Objects and people can be distinguished, and are seen as separate entities.

The time of shyness has begun. The child responds in a reserved way or even with loud crying if someone other than the familiar carer picks him up. This may even apply to a familiar baby-sitter or grandparent. Not only is there an expansion of awareness of the surrounding world, but also an increasing amount of space is explored by means of shuffling, rolling or crawling.

Pitfall

Problems may arise when separation anxiety is not properly recognized and when a parent reacts emotionally to the emotion of the child.

Around fourteen months

A new step is taken in the awareness process: the child begins to acquire place-oriented memory. For the first time, an event that repeats itself at the same place and time is recognized and greeted with pleasure. For example, the child will stretch his arms to the safety belt when he is lifted into the highchair if he is used to this routine during meal times. This child wants to use his memory, and he participates readily in both good and less good habits. If there is any deviation in the fixed routine for going to sleep, such as an extra song or more drinking, he will remember this the following evening and claim this newly-won privilege.

> *Pitfall*
>
> Without a fixed sleeping routine as a recognizable beacon, the child will display an increasing hunger for songs, bedtime stories, etc. If you concede to this, problems with falling and remaining asleep may arise.

Standing for the first time

Some children are so enthusiastic about standing up that they will not lie in bed, and repeatedly stand up. Even in the middle of the night you may find them standing at the edge of their bed. At the moment when they are on the edge of being awake, they animate themselves by the 'enthusiasm' in their legs. If these children are laid to sleep again with a drink of water or a pacifier, they become used to this routine and wake up again the next night. Before you know it, a waking-sleeping pattern can arise resulting in fatigue and irritability on the part of both the parents and child. In contrast, by devoting no attention or only limited attention to such happenings and by using a suitable sleeping bag, the child will tend to fall asleep again himself.

Pitfall

As a result of well-meaning but erroneous attention, an irresistible enthusiasm for standing up may lead to undesired habits and eventual problems in falling or staying asleep.

The 'No' stage (two to three years old)

The child has now reached the age of two or three years old. Until now, he has lived in a world dominated by 'we.' The surroundings corresponded to his own person. Now he begins gradually to distinguish himself from his parents and other people. He is about to discover the world of 'me' and 'you.' He calls himself by his own name, refers to himself as 'me' and finally as 'I.' You could say that his sense of ego awakens. And it wakes up at the limits. The child wants to, and must, collide with the 'other.' If the child always gets what he wants, he will not learn about himself in relation to the other. The child will become increasingly unruly in its natural search for boundaries. The parent has to get used to this behaviour, to put it mildly. Occasionally, it seems that the child is being deliberately awkward. He suddenly seems to want everything or nothing. His favourite food is rejected and he is adamant about playing with the car that his younger sister has in her hands. When he finally receives it, he shows no interest. Yesterday, he stuck his thumb in his mouth when it was time for an afternoon nap, now he yells 'I don't want to go to sleep!'

> *Pitfall*
> If the wishes of the child become equal with the wishes of the parent in this stage, the child will become increasingly recalcitrant due to his natural yearning for boundaries. Eating and sleeping problems may arise. The child takes control of the household.

Actions to help avoid the pitfalls

Here are a few tips aimed at avoiding some of the pitfalls mentioned above.

Understanding your child's body language

You child cannot yet speak so he cannot articulate exactly what he needs or how he is getting along, but he can do so via his body language. Accordingly, he has his own way of expressing his displeasure or contentment. It is, however, often difficult for adults to understand what the child is 'saying.' We can learn to understand his body language by 'exploratory listening.' Do not immediately offer a helping hand when the child squeals for the umpteenth time because he wants something. Make it a habit to wait a moment. Take a deep breath and plant your feet solidly on the ground. By remaining cool, you can take an objective look at the body language of your child in all kinds of situations. This basic tranquillity will allow you to assess the situation better and to make the right decision. You can also exercise your perception when your child is not asking anything of you, simply by watching at a 'loving distance.' Every day you should take the time to observe your playing or sleeping child without interjecting your own trains of thought. You may see the relaxed face of your sleeping child suddenly frowning and hear a couple of yells. His eyes may even open. Then you will notice, perhaps to your own surprise, that he has not woken up, and has fallen into a deep sleep once more. In this way you can discover that your well-intentioned lifting from bed, to which you were accustomed, is not always necessary and can even disrupt the child's sleep.

Helping your child by not helping

'Helping your child by not helping' is a statement by a mother that I can fully endorse. Not helping her child was not an easy matter, she informed me, as she had a great tendency to try to spare her children any kind of grief. Many parents will probably recognize this. 'Helping your child by not helping' is a healthy point of departure to postpone giving help, where the situation allows it, and perhaps to avoid giving it altogether if possible. As a result, the child is given the opportunity to learn to solve his own small problems. Instead of dependence, the development of your child's ability to cope is stimulated, which is extremely important. You can actually begin this technique right from the birth of the child. You do not need to respond to every howl. Allow your child his own frowns and small frustrations without lavishing undue attention or comfort. In such situations, helping is not always the best solution.

What do we mean by an ability to cope, in this context? A child that has had enough to drink and is not tired is capable of playing on his own without whining or demanding attention. If this child is tired and is put to bed when awake, he will learn to fall asleep on its own. In short, the child will manage to cope. A child that cannot cope will need the extended arm of the parent: he cannot be alone and can only fall in sleep in his parents' arms. There is the risk that this child will take control of the household and he, instead of the parents, will dictate the daily routines. This may even result in some kind of twenty-four-hour entertainment programme organized by the parents. One mother articulated this as: 'my child continually plugs into my energy.'

Of course, this does not mean that cuddling and playing with your child should be taken off the menu, but it does mean that the child's ability to cope will be improved. Besides time for playing together and receiving attention, there should also be time for playing alone or looking around, before the child goes to sleep. Every healthy child can amuse himself, regardless of how small he may be, if he gets the chance to learn by experience and recognition. A child who learns to amuse himself develops self-confidence and has the opportunity to explore his increasingly expanding world. And you will also have a moment for yourself. Leaving your child to amuse himself does not mean that you have cut the emotional ties. You remain bound to your child even if he is sleeping upstairs. And you can remain in contact by giving a smile, singing a song, or caressing his head as you pass by the playpen. Experiencing and overcoming small frustrations are as much part of a child's world as they are of an adult's world. It is impossible to grow up without frustration. Overprotection means that you are robbing your child of the chance to develop. Moreover, you are spending your own energy.

Avoid the projection of your own emotions

It is all too easy to take our own feelings as standard and project our own emotions on to the child. However, to a certain extent the soul of a child is alien to us. We have outgrown this phase, and we can no longer place ourselves in that situation. We can no longer feel, think and want as an infant. We can only guess what a baby experiences or is conscious of. We are all too eager to ascribe to a child what we borrow from our own experience. 'He is crying because he wants to be with us at the table. He is lonely in his bed.' In saying this, we are allowing the child to think, feel and want as if he were a complete human in a small form.

In the following example, a mother ascribed a sleeping problem to her child on the basis of her own sleeping problems. Her child's sleeping problem had soon become a fact due to force of habit. During a maternity visit, I encountered her holding her two-week-old baby in front of her in an unnatural floating position, with only the feet resting on her knees, without the security of her lap. She tried the whole day long to lull her baby to sleep in this position, which she claimed he found the most pleasant.

She confided:

> 'I sleep poorly because I cannot relax. My son is exactly the same. He cannot fall asleep without help. We often have him in our arms, he isn't in bed much. But if we can make him a little bit happy, we're pleased to make the effort.'

Allow scope for Rest, Rhythm, Respect and Regulations

R for Rest

The R for Rest simply means ensuring sufficient repose by means of a healthy alternation of sleeping and being awake, as well as by means of living in a tranquil, not-too-busy environment. In short, you should create a world in which your child can cope with the stimuli he receives. As a parent, you are needed in order to ensure that both take place, because your child cannot close himself off from too many stimuli. Too many experiences are unsettling, and can result in stomach cramps, overactive behaviour or difficulty in sleeping. For example, you may discover that more than one excursion a day is simply too much for a baby.

R for Rhythm

In dealing with your child, the R for Rhythm, in combination with uniformity or routine, is of great assistance in ensuring the necessary rest. They can function as basic principles in everyday affairs. Routine furnishes your child with a sense of security and trust in himself and his environment. If the child is generally contented, an occasional deviation from the routine will do no harm. For example, you may need to wake the child up so that you can collect his brother from playschool. This should be an exception rather than a rule.

Rhythm and uniformity in dealing with your child is the key theme running through this book. I shall return to it frequently.

What do I mean by **rhythm?**

The same events in the same order:
Sleeping, being awake, feeding, cuddling or comforting in one's arms or on one's lap, playing alone in the playpen, becoming tired, being laid to sleep while still awake.

What do I mean by **uniformity?**

The same event at the same place, such as the baby always playing on his own in the playpen, sleeping in the same bed during the daytime, and sleeping in the same place at night, for example.

R for Respect

Respect has two aspects: respect for your child and respect for yourself as a parent.

As a unique being, your child deserves respect. You should join in with what your child is doing rather than taking extra playing initiatives yourself. Go along with your child; your child's game remains his own game and not yours. Do not pass your child around (even if it is sleeping) if you have visitors. If he is ready to sleep, allow him to rest in bed.

Respect for yourself is the other aspect and no less important. Respect is often difficult to find when you are consistently busy with your baby, being subservient. For example:

'Alex never slept on his own, even from his earliest days. He would only sleep in the sling and at night he slept with us in our bed. We noticed that he was soon bored with things, at least that is how we labelled his behaviour. He often cried, was tense, was restless and I was busy with him for more or less the whole day. He had a lot of trouble with stomach cramps, we thought. We tried to alleviate that with homeopathic drops. The remedy was — as was the case with almost every-thing — to walk around with him in the sling until we dropped. If he eventually fell asleep during the day, we walked on tiptoe through the house.'

The example illustrates that the parent has offered herself up completely and lost all respect for herself. By turning the tide, the mother can regain some breathing space. If she respects her own being, she can use this newly-won time to build up her own energy. In Alex's case, the tide was turned by swaddling him in conjunction with introducing rhythm and uniformity in dealing with him. How did this develop further? In the mother's words:

'When I swaddled him for the first time, he slept for four hours in one go. Alex calmed down with a com-bination of a strict timetable of sleeping, feeding and playing. The cramps disappeared overnight and his ten-sion decreased enormously after about a week. He now has enough energy to go exploring things by himself. I too have regained my energy and good mood and my relationship with my husband has improved greatly.'

R for Regulation

This R was presented to me by a parent. Regulation means taking the initiative and setting limits. It has nothing to do with exercising power or misusing your authority, as one might imagine, but with taking responsibility. You, as a parent, should know what your child needs. If the limits are not clear, your child will gradually take control of the household and dictate events instead of the parents.

To summarize, the application of the four Rs will make life more predictable for your child. You will know what to expect and your child will too. This predictability will help your child to gain a feeling of safety and security, which form the basis for gaining confidence in himself and in the world in general. If things are predictable from birth onwards, it will be easy to develop a personal rhythm of sleeping, being awake and feeding. Having enjoyed sufficient feeding, the child will soon be capable of making contact with his environment. When he is tired and is laid in bed at the right time, he will learn to fall asleep on his own without having to be dependent on someone to rock him to sleep. To the baby, the quality of sleep, feeding and the period of being awake with his own independent activities and games are all closely linked. The four Rs are all oriented to this interdependence. Accordingly, excessive crying and restlessness can be prevented.

Routine is still important to a child older than one year who only sleeps once during the day. However, the way in which you promote this predictability does change. The direct satisfaction of hunger is no longer the central issue. The predictability lies in recognizable rituals and the signal for what is going to happen. Singing or playing the same song when the child is laid to sleep conveys the message:

the games are over, it is time to sleep. And the child will go to sleep. He is now accustomed to going to sleep with this specific song with the same words, so that he will not think of doing anything else. In addition, a one or two-year-old welcomes the joy of recognition as he exercises his memory. He 'scores,' as it were, when he has guessed correctly what is going to happen.

3. The senses as gateway to the soul

Healthy sensory development is of essential importance for the baby to feel at home in his own body. On this basis, he will secure his own place in the world with a healthy interaction between himself and the world. The senses are often referred to as the gateway to the soul, allowing us to perceive ourselves and the world around us.

By investigating the significance of the sense of touch in particular, the so-called 'life sense' and sleep, I gradually became aware of the importance of limiting a small child during his sleep. By this, I mean limiting him by tucking him in well, in combination with a sleeping bag, a wrap, or swaddling if necessary.

Rudolf Steiner, the founder of anthroposophy, described seven other senses in addition to the five familiar ones — hearing, vision, taste, touch and smell — including the senses of balance, motion and the life sense. The life sense conveys perceptions such as comfort and discomfort, fatigue or lack of it, and so on. Discussing these senses is outside the scope of this book. To anyone who is interested, I recommend the book *The Twelve Senses* by Albert Soesman.[3]

Development of the senses in the first seven years

In the first seven years of life, the emphasis lies on those senses that are oriented primarily to the perception of our own corporality: the life sense, and the senses of touch, motion and balance. I shall not cover the sense of balance here. The structure and the feeling of being 'at home' in one's body are the central issues here. At the same time, the child comes into contact with the environment via his body by touching, tasting and looking. The young child is a receptive creature and is at one with the world around him. He doesn't only experience what he sees and hears but is also sensitive to the moods and intentions of others. In himself, a child moves with everything that happens all around him and responds to these stimuli through emulation. In the stage of life before a child learns to speak and think, he cannot distance himself from stimuli from his environment, especially not audible stimuli. A child only learns this gradually as a result of his developing intellect and the ability to name things.

The sense of touch

When a child arrives in this world, his first tactile experience is that of the midwife who guides him and lays him on his mother's stomach. The sense of touch that creates this experience is spread out across the entire surface of his body. The duality of 'myself and the world' is physically experienced by the sense of touch. What kind of feeling is this?

Experiencing one's self

By touching, you experience where your own being ends and the other begins. Small children who lose themselves in the impressions they receive and become restless as a result, can regain their composure by experiencing their own physical limitations. This can be done by embracing them tightly. Larger children will obtain much pleasure from an intensive session of physical play or tickling. In the schoolyard, boisterous children continually collide with other children, often to the great irritation of the latter. This colliding is not a form of bullying but rather an expression of the need to experience one's own limits. Via these collisions, they can assure themselves of the fact 'I am me, I exist.' The pressure of the tightly tucked-in blanket in bed, the limitations of the right-sized sleeping bag, or of the swaddling wraps give the child a feeling over his whole body of 'this is my house, this is me' with every little movement. This recurring certainty gives him a feeling of trust in himself and in the world. Such experiences are essential for a growing feeling of well-being.

Experiencing the outside world

The small child is interested in everything and wants to touch, grab, hold or bite everything within reach. By exploring the world in this way, a sense of reality is developed along with an awareness of what is real and what is not. Grabbing and exploring are needed in order to understand things, name them, conceive of them, and remember them. 'Nourishment' for the sense of touch helps in the development of interest and respect for the world — playthings made of natural materials can work well.

When the small child is treated caringly, cuddled and cherished, and his skin is well looked after, the fundamental knowledge of being safe-and-sound will grow. The child will be able to become attached to other people. If these positive tactile experiences do not take place, this may result in over-vulnerability, anxiety and lack of interest in the world. Early and rich tactile experience of the world seems to produce the frame of reference for exploring social situations later in life. Someone who is good at this is said to be 'tactful.'

The life sense

The life sense lets us know how we are doing physically by making us aware of our inner experiences. It generates the link between our inner essence and our body. The body is regarded as belonging to us and we feel at one with it. If this link is not made, the body will always feel somewhat alien to the person in question. It does not belong to him, he is not settled comfortably in it, and he usually has a diminished sense of pain. In short, a healthy life sense makes it possible to rest in oneself at a very basic level. Another experience of the life sense is the natural relationship with time. Under normal circumstances, being refreshed usually follows fatigue, hunger is replaced by satisfaction. Daytime follows dark night. The life sense allows us to rely upon the self-evident flow of time.

With a baby, we see just how important this sense is for his development. When a child feels secure and comfortable, a well-developed life sense will be a compass for his further life. If we are healthy, the life sense gives us a harmonious physical feeling of power and energy. We feel refreshed after a healthy sleep. Hunger can gnaw at us. When it is satisfied, a benevolent feeling of satisfaction arises. Life flows on, we can take on the world, a healthy warmth spreads through our body. The greater the hunger, the greater the intensity of satisfaction. The life sense receives a positive impulse in the first years of life by providing good care, tender physical contact, attention and warmth, and the application of a regular rhythm of sleeping, being awake and feeding.

'After the first time she slept the whole night, after a lengthy period of being restless, Merel again had rosy cheeks and radiated contentment as she once did. She was eleven weeks old. We felt like we had regained our little girl.'

The sense of motion

The movements of a newborn are completely uncoordinated. You could say that although the child is not yet moving, something is moving the child. The reflex movements, by means of which the child indicates that he wants to drink, are also something passive. It is a milestone when a child of around three months old sees his hands passing by his nose and can stop them there, only to set them in motion once again with bated breath. The child can now learn to make purposeful movements. In this learning process, being able to stop the movement in order to perceive exactly what is happening, albeit subconsciously, is just as important as starting up a movement. During these small pauses, the child's sense of motion informs him of the position and movement of the limbs with regard to his own body, and of the relationship of one muscle to the other. It teaches him (subconsciously) to know about the nature of each movement. In a child that is subject to uncoordinated movement, where there are no pauses in movement, this learning process scarcely occurs. Many children learn to introduce these pauses on their own, others have to be assisted.

To a child who has his hands under control, the baby-gym that he can reach for and grab in the playpen is a favourite toy. The discovery of the feet soon follows. Finally, the child learns to make increasingly complex movements of rolling over, crawling, standing up and walking. Due to the 'memory' of well-developed sense of motion, the movements gradually become routine and thus fluent. A good illustration of this is the difficult process of learning to write. Once we have learned this, the words flow out of the pen without us having to pay attention to coordination.

In addition to his own movement, a child also learns to perceive movements and forms in the outside world. A healthy development of a child's own sense of motion is essential here. When a child's eyes scan a shape in the distance, or when an object within reach is explored with the hands, the sense of motion also plays a role here. The senses of motion, vision and touch work together.

> With a well-developed sense of motion, the child is the helmsman on his own ship.

In general, the sense of motion does not need to be stimulated. It is usually the case that the development of this sense requires only sufficient rest and sleep. An excess of movement in the environment will cause a rather one-sided development of the sense of motion. For example, the sense of motion of the eyes is sometimes excessively advanced at the cost of general physical development. This can easily occur when babies are placed in the rocking chair or first-stage car seat for too long. As a result, the freedom of movement of the child's own body is limited while the child can watch everything that is going on. Often there is a mobile near him that is continually set in motion. After some time, the child's eyes will become dominant. Pleasure in moving his own body will fade, and sense of self-motion declines. The child will increasingly demand to be entertained and stimulated by movement in his surroundings.

It is of the utmost importance that the child generates his pattern of movement in his own good time and in his own way. Sitting for lengthy periods in the rocking seat and placing a child in a seated position while he cannot yet sit up himself can have adverse effects on the development of the sense of motion.

'When my child was eight weeks old, I genuinely thought that she was playing with the baby-gym that hung above her head in the playpen. I found that she could amuse herself quite well. She repeatedly struck it, and hit it harder and harder. I though she was becoming more active due to her enthusiasm. Now she is four weeks older and more at rest due to the fact she is sleeping more, which is due to the rhythm we have managed to instil. Now I can see the difference. Previously she was only milling with her arms and struck the baby-gym purely by chance because it was so near her in the playpen. I couldn't see that she was completely subordinate to these actions, that she couldn't retreat from the stimulation, and that she was becoming overtired as a result. Now I can recognize that she moves her hand deliberately toward the objects and takes genuine pleasure in her games.'

4. Sleep

A child's behaviour and appearance indicate whether or not a child is getting enough sleep. Overactive behaviour and alert eyes are often not recognized as signs of over-tiredness. They are often erroneously taken to be expressions of inquisitiveness and thus as something positive. This same child may tend to grow slowly. That is no surprise as it is sometimes claimed that he is devoting all his energy to this curiosity. This child, sometimes only three months old, seems inexhaustible and scarcely sleeps during the day. In contrast, he falls asleep immediately in the evening and sleeps until the following morning. It is striking that this child is considerably calmer in the first few hours of the morning and becomes increasingly animated as the day wears on.

There are many misconceptions about sleep. Sometimes people say: 'You can't get a baby to sleep less or more. You have to get used to a new, active family member.' The following example illustrates the contrary, and is in keeping with other experiences I have heard of.

Anna, six weeks old:
Prior to a period of swaddling and the introduction of routine: Anna cries and whines for five hours, sleeps for ten hours, and is entertained for six of the twenty-four hours.

Two weeks after the introduction of the new regime: Anna cries and whines for two hours (60 percent less), sleeps for fifteen hours (50 percent more) and is entertained for two of the twenty-four hours.

Her father recounts:

'Instead of a discontented cry-baby she is now a beautifully peaceful child with a fixed sleeping pattern. My own contact with her has become much more pleasurable because we are both fitter.'

A closer look at sleep

Sleep is a recurring state of repose accompanied by a decrease in consciousness. We close ourselves off to all influences from the outside world.[4] Sleep itself fluctuates between a deep and light form. When in a light sleep, we hover at the threshold of consciousness but we normally do not wake up. Perhaps we turn over in bed. A child's bed may creak, he may mutter something or even open his eyes, only to fall back again into a deeper sleep.

Newborn children begin with light sleep, also referred to as Rapid Eye Movement (REM) sleep. The eyes move quickly, breathing accelerates, and random muscle movements occur. The child may seem to be awake but he is asleep. An 'angelic smile' may appear on his face.[5] Without the tactile limitation of a tight blanket, for example, the child may easily wake up in this phase, as the following quote describes:

> 'When I was observing my six-week-old daughter in sleep, I saw the following: she sank into sleep but rose to the surface due to uncontrolled arm movements. When I held her arms tight, she fell into a deep sleep again within a minute!'

The REM phases play an essential role in the processing of information and in learning processes. In a young child, the subconscious experiences of the day are transformed into the learning processes of the night, such as developing motor skills and mastering language. Infants spend more than half of their sleeping time in REM sleep. At around six months, REM sleep accounts for around 30 percent of sleep (in adults it is 20–25 percent).

The deep sleep is the Non-Rapid Eye Movement (NREM) phase. In this phase, the body is resting. There is little movement and the heartbeat and rate of breathing are slow and regular. Physical recovery and growth take place. With children, the level of growth hormone increases in the first hours of sleep, when the NREM phase lasts the longest. If this sleep is interrupted, an immediate decrease in the amount of growth hormone occurs. When sleep is regained, this returns to the old levels. Thus, deep sleep is essential for growth.

Is there a night-day rhythm or a sleeping-awake rhythm in infants?

When we talk about a night-day rhythm and make this the basis for our actions, we are ignoring the real needs of the baby. He will not obtain the amount of sleep he really requires. The following example demonstrates this. In my opinion, it is better to speak of a 'sleeping-awake' rhythm. Each sleeping period should actually be a form of nocturnal experience.

Roy, three months old:

'During the day, I keep our three-month-old son, Roy, with us in the living room. Now and again he falls asleep in his playpen. I think it is quite normal to have him around! Daytime life happens in the living room, nocturnal life upstairs. In this way he will learn the difference between night and day and he will fall asleep quicker.

If I put Roy into bed, it is as if he doesn't belong here.
Then I see him so little. When can I see him and pay him
some attention?'

The time that a child is awake is part of the daytime
and all sleeping time — even sleeping during the
day — belongs to nocturnal life.

With the consistent application of predictable routine, the
evening and night feed will disappear as the child grows
older (at around six months) and the daytime life of your
child will occupy an increasing number of hours. The quality of life during the day depends on the degree of rest a
child takes, which, in turn, is based on going to sleep at the
right times and for long enough, and on receiving enough
food. Your growing child will thus participate increasingly
in family life during the day, in a natural way and at his
own rate. And the evening and the night will belong to the
parents (at least for the first twelve years!).

The duration of sleep

In the first two weeks, the newborn is mainly rather drowsy
and only really 'wakes up' in order to feed. A six-week-
old child usually has periods of being awake between 7am
(07:00) and 7pm (19:00) After the 7pm (19:00) feed, the
child will normally retire for the night, albeit with an interruption for one or two nighttime feeds. After the feed, the
child should fall asleep once more, at least if it is accustomed
to being put to bed again without any further attention.

The average duration of sleep per twenty-four hours for children who have some routine in their lives is as follows:

Newborns: around 20 hours

3 months old: around 18 hours

6 months old: around 16 hours

14 to 42 months old: 14 hours

The ability to fall asleep and remain asleep is determined by hormones. When we feel lethargic and sleepy in the evening, the cortisone level in our blood has decreased. As a result, we can leave behind the activities of the day and surrender to a beneficial sleep. In cases of overfatigue due to stress or a shortage of sleep, we have an increased level of cortisone in our blood, which impedes falling asleep. The stress of sleeplessness that then arises causes an increase in the hormone epinephrine. As a result, we experience an apparently heightened alertness that camouflages the mental fatigue. As far as I know, this mechanism applies to both adults and children. As an adult, you are capable of a great deal of activity as a consequence of this heightened alertness — as long as it lasts. The main reason that a child stays awake and 'alert' for longer is the increased stimulation he receives from his parents, resulting in the disruption of the rhythm of sleeping and being awake. Ultimately there arises a vicious circle of chronic shortage of sleep, fatigue, irritation and heightened sensitivity in both the child and his parents.[6]

All sleeping problems are waking problems

In general, you can say that all sleeping problems are actually waking problems. Healthy sleep is helped by good interaction between activity and relaxation, between liveliness and tranquillity, between watchfulness and being carefree, between eating and an empty stomach.

---

5. The link between sleeping and feeding stands or falls with rhythm and uniformity

Experience indicates that much restlessness and crying comes from the parents' lack of knowledge about the link between feeding and sleeping. They are unaware of the fact that this link and the quality of both activities stand or fall with predictable routine.

This chapter can help prevent such feeding and sleeping problems. The discussion about feeding is mainly referring to breast-feeding.

Many mothers start breastfeeding enthusiastically but stop after about three months. In conversations with these mothers I often hear that they did not have to stop: they would have continued if they had known better, if they had been better supervised. If, if, if ... This is a great pity, especially when the mother was greatly motivated.

Breastfeeding is a natural process. Nevertheless, you do need information because it is no longer a custom that is passed on from mother to daughter. In addition you need to understand the link between feeding and sleeping. In my opinion, this is not addressed enough in current education. A child who has had sufficient sleep will enthusiastically drink the amount he needs within half an hour and will then release the nipple as a sign of satisfaction. The child can then lie awake contented, and then fall asleep for two hours before again waking up hungry. Conversely, a child who has many short naps during the day will not get enough healthy sleep, and so may stay at the breast for a long time, more asleep than awake. His apparent drinking is more sucking than actually drinking. Ultimately, the activity of sucking will cause the tired child to fall asleep with a stomach that is not full. After a nap of scarcely half an hour, he will again want to feed. This child is never truly satisfied or refreshed. He will whine more and more, and enter a negative spiral of crying, feeding and sleeping less. Some mothers say 'I have enough milk, my child is often at my breast for an hour!' That is when I begin to suspect that things are going wrong.

Feeding on demand

With 'feeding on demand,' supply and demand are usually well attuned to one another. Breastfeeding itself is qualitatively good and adapted to the age of the child. The feeding for a child that is born too early is different from that of a three-month-old child. Feeding on demand, however, is not as free of obligation as the term might imply. Some parents are wrong-footed by this method. By taking the phrase literally an unlimited freedom may arise without a recognizable feeding pattern — 'ask and you will be given, as long and as often as you wish.' Sometimes one cannot estimate how many feeds are needed or how long the feed will last. A child may learn to come for a feed consisting of a few gulps, and relax into a catnap in-between.

Besides the frequent, short drinkers, there are also children who attach themselves to the breast for an hour whilst only drinking now and again. The child may spend a large part of this time asleep, sucking only occasionally. The parents gradually lose their organization. The mother gets the feeling that she is continually engaged in breastfeeding. In such situations, too little milk will be generated because the child doesn't drink sufficiently or for long enough.

However, with a healthy approach, feeding on demand is preferable to feeding according to a timetable. If supply and demand are well attuned to one another, the child will develop his own rhythm within a few weeks of birth, which will be roughly the same every day. As a parent, you will know what to expect. If you follow the child's own rhythm, you will not need to wake him up to fit into your timetable. And you will not have to make your child wait after he has woken from a healthy sleep simply because the hour has not yet struck. The method is much more 'child-friendly.' And when your breastfeeding gradually diminishes or your child needs more, you can be sure that he will wake up sooner to be fed. Finally, your growing child will eventually indicate when the evening feed is no longer necessary. The decline in waking up and interest in breastfeeding will be a running theme here.

How can you ensure that feeding on demand will not lead to unlimited freedom without a recognizable drinking pattern? Sit down in a quiet corner without disturbing factors such as the television or the telephone. Pay attention to what is happening. And keep an eye on the time. You will soon learn, when there has been enough milk, when the child's drinking is effective, and when the child is only sucking. You will discover that breastfeeding takes place in three stages.

Putting the child to the breast

Do not allow your child to keep on sucking air, but guide him to your nipple with the arm on which his head is resting, the moment his mouth opens. Look for a compromise between holding the child loosely and taking it in a stranglehold, as strict nurses used to do. The most common feeding position is the so-called 'Madonna position,' where the mother sits up straight. If the child is drinking from the left breast, lay him on your left forearm with his head in the hollow of your elbow. Support his back and buttocks with your left arm and hand. Fill up your lap with cushions if necessary, and ensure support for your feet so that you can sit in a comfortable position without having to lift up your child. It is important that the child should lie with his belly against yours. Small variations on this theme are possible. The proportions of the arms and the size of the breasts also play a role.

The three stages of breastfeeding

The first stage

This is characterized by rapid, superficial jaw movements without a break. The nipple and a part of the areola are completely engulfed and the mouth creates a vacuum. The child's lips are curled outwards. Milk does not arrive immediately. These stimuli activate the lactation reflex. Many mothers experience this as a 'sweet' pain in the breast, whereas some women do not feel any reflex at all. The lactation reflex ensures that the 'tap' is opened and the milk begins to flow.

The second stage

This stage is typified by less rapid, but nevertheless more powerful, movements in which the jaws move even right up to the ears. Usually after three or four 'draws,' the milk collected in the mouth is rhythmically swallowed without the nipple being released. The chin relaxes and drops a little and the sound of swallowing becomes audible. If there is an overflow of milk, it is sometimes necessary to take an eager child from the breast for a couple of seconds in order to avoid choking and sputtering. Keep your child in the same position close to the breast so that he can get back to business when his mouth is empty and before he becomes impatient — his food has been stolen! The continued drinking usually takes place more moderately, interrupted by small, recurrent pauses for swallowing. There are also children who continue to drink uniformly without seeming to stop to swallow.

The third stage

This stage resembles the first stage, except only the mouth is moving and there are no breaks for swallowing. If the child drinks efficiently, he will release the nipple after twenty or thirty minutes at the most. Your breast is, to all intents and purposes, empty, even if a couple of drops may appear when he has let go. Some children drink so eagerly that the breast is emptied in five to ten minutes. You should then allow the child time to release a burp. If that doesn't happen within a few minutes, you can give your child the other breast. If too much time is allowed for burping, the child may fall asleep. If this happens, you will not be able to give him the other breast, so try to avoid this. Experience indicates that, in general, breast-feeding works best when both breasts are used for feeding. Your child will drink from the second breast for a shorter period. You can regard this as dessert, but certainly one that should not be skipped.

The next feed should begin with the breast with which you ended the previous time. If there is an intermediary feed or a temporary comforting — which I regard as an exception to the rule — the last breast should still be offered.

When you pay attention to your breastfeeding and keep an eye on the clock, you can stimulate your child to take a complete meal within a continuous acceptable time. In that case, your child will develop his own regular sleeping and drinking pattern within a few weeks. After a good sleep, he will be refreshed and will present himself to be fed. This will usually be every three or four hours. After a good feed, he will be completely satisfied. And following a period of drowsiness on your lap, he will be able to lie awake, satisfied with himself, without having to be entertained.

The number of feeds a day

In the first few days after birth, the baby will want to be fed eight to twelve times a day. The production of milk will come into full swing after about three or four days. Your breasts will become fuller and rounder and you may have difficulty with engorgement. If your baby can drink well, he will soon be able to empty the breast. He will eventually assume a rhythm in which he will take six to eight feeds a day. Most babies drink more often in the afternoons and evenings that they do in the morning. If breastfeeding is effective, the baby will require at least six feeds a day for the first few months.

Adjusting within the time limits from two to four hours. (This also applies to bottle feeding).

With a child who only drinks a little at a time, you need to extend the in-between times so that he learns what true hunger is. He will then tend to take a complete feed. You should stick to an in-between time of at least two hours, calculated from the beginning of the previous feed. This will allow the digestive processes a certain amount of rest. This rule does not apply if there is too little breastfeeding during the first few days after birth. In this case, you should feed your child more often.

Children who sleep too long during the day sometimes have to be woken up to be fed. In that case, you should take four hours from the beginning of the previous feed as the maximum period between feeds. In the night you can wait until your baby 'checks in,' with the exception of children who do not yet weigh ten pounds. Why do we have a limit of four hours? A child may sleep for six hours in a row during the day. He will then wake up more often wanting to be fed in the night because he has consumed so little during the day. In doing so, the night-day rhythm will be reversed — an unwelcome development.

Restlessness at the breast

Your child may become restless at your breast either during or after drinking. He may cry or overstretch himself. Your production of milk may not yet be in full swing or may be declining. The child will continue to make eager attempts based on a healthy survival mechanism. The position at your breast or his drinking technique may not be completely right, or your child may be suffering from cramps. There may be nipple problems and/or thrush. In such situations, it is advisable to go to the health centre or to ask advice from a lactation expert. Do not waste too much time fussing about as any delay will have an adverse effect on breastfeeding.

Too little milk

Your milk may have declined without you noticing it. In that case, your hungry child will pull intensely at the nipple after a relatively short drinking time, will release it with a whimper and then attack it once again. A spirited child will continue to make passionate attempts to drink. More frequent requests for feeding, which become more obvious due to shorter periods of sleep than your child is used to, may mean that your milk is insufficient. In such cases, take your child to your breast more often. This will mean a couple of extra feeds a day. Looking after yourself or giving yourself a treat for a couple of days can help enormously. If there is nothing else wrong, your milk will be up to par again within a couple of days.

Growth spurts

According to the literature, so-called 'growth spurts' can occur at the ages of ten to fourteen days, six weeks, and around three months. At these times the child will therefore want more breastfeeding. They usually only last for two days and your child may need to be helped to concentrate on the feed. Breastfeeding can only be stimulated by sufficient and eager feeding.

If, however, your child is given the opportunity to take a sip when he wants, chaos can easily arise. That is what happened to a mother who came for advice. She hesitantly said: 'Then the more frequent feeding days began, but when do they stop?' She had been busy for three weeks! Even during growth spurts you can take the above-mentioned minimum period of two hours between feeds as a rule. If you have not returned to an acceptable rhythm within three days, you should ask for advice from the health centre. A bad habit is easily acquired but is difficult to shake off.

I find it remarkable that these growth spurts are also said to apply to the ages of six weeks and three months. Six weeks is the age at which a child begins to make contact via laughs and smiles. It is an expression of the first awakening from its own twilight world and the arrival in our world. The age of three months is a second moment of wakening to the world. The child begins to take an interest in things in his wider surroundings, and discovers his own hands. It is no longer the pure satisfaction of hunger that is the central issue. After a slight feed, it is time to give the world a smile. With a hearty laugh, the nipple will slip out of the child's mouth and the hands will grope around at the breast and stomach of the mother. If the telephone rings, the child will release the nipple. These expressions of awakening to the world are extremely endearing and invite the mother to respond. If the interaction continues too long, the child will be less inclined to resume drinking and will subsequently request feeding more often.

Can we talk about growth spurts or would it be better to talk about 'awakening-to-the-world' days?

A guideline for the sleeping, waking and feeding rhythm in the first year of life

Up to one year old, the quality of the child's sleep, his play, and his feeding habits are closely linked. The rhythm and uniformity described in this book are directed toward this interdependence.

The following framework has been taken from life itself. Children with rhythm and uniformity in their lives demonstrate this kind of sleeping, waking and feeding rhythm. If your child is one who takes lots of naps, you will probably not believe that a child can sleep so much. Nevertheless, do not assume in advance that this framework is something that is incompatible with your child.

In this framework, the following points are important:

✿ feeding takes place only when the child wakes up, perhaps with a change of nappies in between
✿ the waking time is the feeding time during the day, followed by the time for play or lying awake
✿ the night is the time between approximately 8pm (20:00) and 7am (07:00) perhaps interrupted by a nocturnal feeding without play

In the following framework, any evening crying sessions have been omitted.

After the first morning feed, a number of children will skip the playing session and will fall asleep again immediately. They extend their night-time in this way. As indicated previously, all sleeping periods are *nocturnal* life, including the sleeping periods during the day.

0–2 weeks	Duration of each waking time:	30–45 minutes
	Duration of each sleep:	2–3 hours
	Number of feeds per day:	8–6

2–6 weeks	Duration of each waking time:	45–60 minutes
	Duration of each sleep:	2–3 hours
	Number of feeds per day:	8–6

7–12 weeks	Duration of each waking time:	60–75 minutes
	Duration of each sleep:	2–3 hours
	Number of feeds per day:	6–5

3–5 months	Duration of each waking time:	$1\frac{1}{2}$ hours
	Duration of each sleep:	2 hours
	Number of feeds per day:	5

At around six months, children begin to skip the afternoon sleep. After the four o'clock (16:00) feed, they stay awake until the next feeding at around six-thirty (18:30). It will be self-evident that after such a long period of being awake, you should feed your child before he is put to bed. A number of children have difficulty in waking up for the late evening feed, which is then abandoned.

When an afternoon sleep has become part of a child's daily rhythm, going to bed directly from the highchair where he has had lunch, you will be able to maintain this routine until the age of around three-and-a-half, at least if the parents remain firm in their approach to their child during the 'No' stage of their two-year-old, a characteristic element of this age. Resistance to this approach will be short-lived. Experience shows that most children of this age benefit from this rest.

6 months

Duration of each waking time: 2 hours
Duration of each sleep: 2 hours
The sleep after the 3rd feeding will gradually vanish
Number of feeds per day: 5–4
The evening feed will gradually vanish

Around 9
months

Duration of each waking time: 2 hours
Duration of each sleep: 2 hours
Number of feeds per day: 4–3
No sleep after the 3rd feed; the night begins at 7 pm

12–14
months

Sleep: Once or twice a day
Number of feeds per day: 3 feeds and 2 'snacks'
The night begins at 7 pm

14–42
months

sleep: One afternoon sleep,
                               2–3 hours
number of feeds per day: 3 feeds and 2 'snacks'
The night begins at 7 pm

6. Crying and comforting

You may wonder whether babies nowadays cry more than they used to. Are there more whining waifs, children who are only content in their parents' arms? Do present-day children 'want' more closeness? Isn't it somewhat unnatural to lay a child in a cot after nine months in the womb? After all, young monkeys hang on their mothers' stomachs for months.

Is it true that babies used to cry less frequently? Or was the attitude different? In olden days, the child had to be hardened to cope with life. Crying was common, it was part and parcel of upbringing. People claimed it was good for the lungs. Moreover, busy mothers had little time to comfort their child, and anyway, the theory went, that only led to spoiled brats.

Why do babies cry?

If a child has a clean nappy and has had enough to eat, why does he cry? Why does he cry when he is left alone or is put to bed? Crying usually begins one or two weeks after birth. Some children cry a lot right from the day they are born. Being born too soon, over-rapid delivery, parents' stress, pregnancy problems or a difficult delivery may be the cause of this. There is often no clear-cut cause. Some parents say things like: 'It is as if my child doesn't feel up to worldly life, as if he recoils from it.'

The child's body language says a lot. He flails his arms and legs. Sometimes his body resembles a hard plank and he clenches his fists frenetically until they are blue.

If an answer is found it is often only a vague suspicion, and certainly not a fact. We do know that excessive crying causes a negative spiral of fatigue in both the parents and the child. This overtiredness clouds the child's body language, so that there is soon no compass to indicate which direction to take.

> 'I don't think of my child as a cry-baby. He does want to be carried around all day, but then he is contented. As soon as I lay him down, he begins to cry. He feels lonely and it seems as if he has to smell me. During the day he only sleeps in my arms or in the sling and at night he sleeps on my stomach. If I didn't have him with me, I think he would cry for twenty-four hours.'

Experience in my own health practice leads me to think that cry-babies do not (or hardly) exist. However, there are babies that display much crying and whining behaviour due to overtiredness.

By removing overtiredness, excessive crying will vanish. The current percentage of cry-babies — 10–25 percent, if you believe the literature — could probably be reduced to less than 5 percent.[7]

Comforting

'You have to comfort your child! If you let your child cry, you are not a good parent!' This impression is created almost every time you open a magazine on parenting. Many parents are only too pleased to accept such tips as these are their only sources of their information. After all, most people have not been educated for this new occupation.

A magazine might say something like:

> 'If your baby cries, he needs comforting. Keep on searching for a way that suits yourself and your baby ...

Many babies have stomach cramps. These usually disappear by the age of three months, although they may last longer. You simply have to accept this. Comfort your child as much as possible. The quicker you comfort him, the more contented he will be later.'

Being comforted is indeed essential to a child. Almost every parent will have a natural inclination to comfort his or her child. After all, a baby is helpless and dependent on his parents. When he is hungry or tired or needs changing, the parents must help him.

Nevertheless, it is not so easy to know which of their child's expressions should be answered with comforting, and which are a request for sleep. For example:

'With our children we have learned that crying is not necessarily a demand to be comforted. In the case of Arthur, who is ten years older than his sister, it took a number of weeks before we realized that his crying could mean: I want to go to bed! It was not necessary to comfort him, give him extra feeding or change him. He simply needed to be laid in his own cot with a pacifier (dummy) and a stroke of his head. With his sister Julia, we knew what to do as soon as she was born. Crying is often a request to be laid in her own cot, regardless of how small she is. Then she is suddenly quiet and sleeps deeply until the next feed. Comforting and holding children often work adversely.'

Over-indulgence

Everyone seems to agree that you cannot over-indulge a baby. But what exactly are we talking about in this context?

You can only really talk about over-indulging a child if a child realizes that he can use crying and whining to get his own way. This implies a certain degree of self-awareness on the part of the child.

Over-indulging is thus possible from the age of around six to nine months. From that age onward, and certainly when the child has acquired a place-oriented memory capability (around fourteen months), one must be wary of over-indulgence. Without noticing it, the sleeping ritual may expand to unwelcome dimensions as the child manages to ask for and obtain more attention. If an extra song is sung two evenings in a row, because your child pleads so charmingly, he will remember this the following evening and will consistently demand that 'extra' song. In this kind of situation, a healthy child will continue to request more and more if the situation repeats itself. In doing so, he learns to manipulate the parents.

Parents do not realize this at first. It is extremely charming and it is easy as a loving parent to concede to this simple request. It is a marvellous and innocent game, just one more song or story! Until you notice that the consequences are becoming less innocent. If you are tired, you will wish that you could go back to the normal ritual but that is no longer possible. Your child will protest and will not easily give up his newly acquired rights.

When parents experience this, they suddenly realize that the time when they can over-indulge their child has arrived.

Habits

Habits arise when the same patterns of action and reaction take place between the parent and child. If your child has the experience of being repeatedly rocked to sleep after crying has led to him being picked up, he will learn that crying will lead to him being picked up and then he will be rocked to sleep. He will become used to being helped to go to sleep and will not learn to fall asleep on his own. Every day you do this, this habit will become stronger. A newborn will become accustomed to this routine within four weeks. The parents of some restless children tell me that, in retrospect, they can see that the habit began at the age of only two weeks.

This is a form of conditioning. A child that is used to falling asleep before being laid in bed will not know what to do when it is placed in bed still awake. It will protest loudly against this unknown situation. Children can become used to drinking lightly at the breast perhaps twelve times a day, but they can also learn to drink five times and take their fill each time. These are all habits. Habits can be both bad and good. Good habits can be used to solve problems of restlessness — as we will see in Part 2 of this book.

My tentative answer to the question: why do children cry?

As mentioned earlier, experience has indicated that many children cry because they are so absolutely tired. If the often-unnoticed cycle of tiredness has been broken and the child gets extra rest, the crying is reduced considerably. The crying that then remains is clearly a form of body language which conveys that the child is hungry, that he is being subjected to too much stimuli or that he wants to go to sleep.

Predictable routine, rest and limitation can help a child feel better and cry less. Part 2 describes how this can be achieved.

Although swaddling itself has not yet been covered, I here present an example to illustrate how crying can be reduced by applying rhythm in the child's life in combination with swaddling.

Does Niels cry because of a birth trauma, or overtiredness or perhaps both? We do not know. His mother summarizes:

> 'Niels was nine pounds at birth. His head appeared but his body seemed to be stuck, The midwife had to pull hard to get him out. In the first few days, he cried no less than ten hours a day and only slept for seven of the twenty-four. He could only fall asleep in my arms, but consistently woke up with a start after a short nap. I was deadbeat after five nights without sleep. The maternity nurse came to visit me when I lay sleeping. She heard our story from the maternity assistant. She decided to swaddle Niels without waking me up. He fell asleep and slept for no less than fifteen hours, albeit with interruptions for feeding. The poor thing was dead tired. What a relief!'

Part 2

Solving Crying and Restlessness

7. Rhythm, uniformity and swaddling

Whereas Part 1 covered the causes of excessive crying and restlessness, this part will deal with ways of solving crying and restlessness that have no medical foundation. It should be clear that it is not aimed at preventing all forms of crying. It may even happen that your child will cry more at the first application of the two methods described here. This should be seen as a healthy protest against something new and unknown. When the problem of restlessness and excessive crying has been solved, 'normal' crying will remain as a kind of body language with a clear message.

My experience is that excessive crying and restlessness are mainly the result of overtiredness. In turn, this overtiredness is mostly a consequence of lack of sleep caused by an irregular pattern of sleeping and drinking, and of the child not being able to fall asleep on his own. Rectifying the problem of crying alone will not remove the underlying cause. The methods described here have the following aims:

* the removal of overtiredness by more sleep
* the promotion of the ability to cope, and thus
* the reduction or disappearance of excessive crying

The methods used here are designed to break old patterns and adopt new patterns. The beneficial effect of these can be retained in the long term if the regularity and clarity that have been applied to solve the problem are continued as components of everyday life.

Two methods ('interventions') are described to turn the tide of excessive crying and restlessness. Both methods use rhythm and uniformity. The only difference between the methods is that one also uses swaddling. See Chapter 11 for the practical aspects of how to swaddle a baby.

---

*What do I mean by **rhythm**?*
The same events in the same order:
   Sleeping, being awake, feeding, cuddling or comforting in one's arms or on one's lap, playing alone in the playpen, becoming tired, being laid to sleep while still awake.

*What do I mean by **uniformity**?*
The same event at the same place, such as the baby always playing on his own in the playpen, sleeping in the same bed during the daytime, and sleeping in the same place at night, for example.

What exactly is swaddling?

Swaddling is when a child that is put to bed is restrained from his shoulders to his toes by two or three cloths in such a way that his body movements are limited. In this way, the child becomes a compact bundle that moves as a whole without the arms and legs flailing around as a result of random reflexes or stomach cramps. The movements are limited by the constraints of the cloths. In this way, the continual self-stimulation due to these movements, which tend to keep a child awake or wake him up too soon, are minimized.

Present-day swaddling compared to traditional methods

In present-day swaddling, as this book demonstrates, the cloths are wound around the arms and legs of the child to a greater or lesser degree of tightness depending on the age of the child. An important differentiation is made in the degree of tightness when the child reaches the age of six months. The child is only swaddled when it is put to bed. Thus, movements are limited when he is ready to rest. When the child is lifted up to be fed and to play, the swaddling clothes are removed, so there is complete freedom of movement. In earlier times, and even today in various cultures, the child was swaddled continuously for a certain period. The child was wrapped up day and night. This period varied from fourteen days to approximately one year. It was often not even necessary to change the child because a slit was left open at the buttocks. The child's entire body was wrapped up, including his head. In contrast to bygone days, swaddling now only takes place if there is a special reason to do so. It is only done during sleeping times and in combination with a predictable routine.

Swaddling itself should be regarded as a temporary aid for the purpose of instilling regularity and an ability to cope. As a result, the child will generate his own rhythm of sleeping, drinking and playing. The wraps become superfluous once rhythm and uniformity have become anchored in the child's daily routine. Of course, the parent remains essential for ensuring regularity in the life of the child.

Up to what age can swaddling be applied?

Most children with whom I have had experience of swaddling were babies aged between three weeks and six months. The group of infants that were swaddled under my supervision is much smaller. Recent research on cry-babies indicates that children of eight months and older should not be swaddled, because of their increasing ability to turn on to their stomachs. Nevertheless, it should be said that swaddling is occasionally good for older children if they suffer greatly from restlessness and stress. In these cases swaddling should be supervised by a doctor or other professional.

I do not know of any research data that indicates that the swaddling of children above a certain age is risky. Nevertheless, it has been demonstrated that a swaddled baby lying on his stomach has a higher risk of cot death. If your child makes an attempt to turn on to his stomach, check the following points, which we shall deal with in more detail shortly:

✿ do his feet protrude from the cloths?
✿ if the child is older than six months, are the cloths tight enough around the legs?
✿ can an arm be wriggled out?
✿ is the blanket large enough?
✿ is the blanket tucked in sufficiently and at the right height?
✿ does the mattress fit, so that the tucked-in blanket stays in place?

Any of these points can make it much easier for the child to turn on to his stomach. Once you have addressed any problems, check your child more often just to see if he is still lying on his back. If your child continues to make attempts to turn on to his stomach, stop the swaddling.

The aim of swaddling is to create a pleasant embrace, an unyielding limitation, and comfortable warmth as a natural follow-on to the womb where the child was also tightly held.

Three types of children who benefit from an intervention

I see many similarities between children who are in need of rhythm and uniformity, whether this is combined with swaddling or not. There are also obvious differences. I shall divide these into three groups: John, Jim and Elizabeth. What I am about to describe are not traits of the children themselves but rather forms of behaviour and characteristics that have arisen due to worsening circumstances over the course of time.

JOHN is a child that takes catnaps, drinks a little when he feels like it, does not grow quickly and his growth is below average.

JIM is a child who frustrates himself continually. His will has become a command, and the parents have to put themselves at his disposal.

ELIZABETH is a 'thriving' child who surpasses all the growth curves in the health centre. She looks contented. She is not a child with problems but her mother scarcely gets a minute's rest.

In more detail:

John

John is eight weeks old when I get to know him. His pale, transparent face radiates great seriousness. The frown on his forehead gives him the appearance of an old man. It is impossible to coax a laugh out of him. His hands and feet are generally quite cold. He is not a child who can lie contented in one's arms. His own arms are one continuous flow of movement, which seems to cause no pleasure whatsoever. He looks fragile but feels muscular. His muscles feel like extremely tense elastic. This is no wonder, since John has constantly been practising sitting up by pushing against his mother's lap. He seems to be unnaturally strong in his arms and legs. He has a surprised look about him and he is very alert and apparently insatiable, so that new entertainment is constantly needed. If he is entertained, he does not cry much. As long as it lasts. Then tiredness takes its toll. He drinks frequently but always too little. He has trouble with stomach cramps and throws up small amounts at irregular times. He scarcely sleeps during the day but does sleep well at night, sometimes seven hours at a stretch.

Jim

Jim is six months old when I meet him. He is a healthy boy who seems pleased to have entered the world. He is a child who does not seem to fit into a little baby's body. He has advanced motor skills. He has been crawling since he was five months old and various teeth have appeared, sometimes a few at the same time. He is a solid, compact boy, a lump of muscle and as strong as a bear. He continually frustrates himself because he wants to do things he cannot yet do. His crying is a deafening howl in which he impressively blows himself up. If he gets his way, this howl is silenced immediately. 'His will has become our command,' confesses his desperate father. 'He never seems to be tired. He hardly sleeps during the day, and he is often awake at night.'

Elizabeth

Elizabeth is four months old when I see her for the first time. Her mother informs me:

> 'My husband and I are exhausted. Up to the age of ten weeks, Elizabeth had six feeds and she slept the whole night. For the last two months — she is now almost four months old — she wants breastfeeding every two hours, day and night. During the day, she drinks for a short time then releases the nipple and looks around with a smile on her face. She doesn't want to drink anymore. She can only amuse herself in the playpen for a short period and if I pick her up and play with her she starts laughing again. When I lay her in bed when she is tired, she begins to shriek. I often have to walk around with her until she sleeps, and sometimes I let her cry in bed. Then she falls asleep after about ten minutes but wakes up again after about half-an-hour. She now has ten feeds a day, four of them during the night.'

Elizabeth is a content, thriving girl with chubby cheeks who does not look tired. She gets more than enough feeding as a result of her frequent drinking. Her weight is far above the average. Her mother looks pale, has bags under her eyes. She tells me despondently that she is stretched to the limit. 'I can't keep this up. What can I do?' On the basis of what I see and what she tells me during the visit, it is clear that she has difficulty in setting limits. Elizabeth thrives on this unlimited, loving attention but her mother can hardly survive.

Elizabeth could also be a bottle-fed child, but these children are mainly breastfed. Constantly having to meet the demand for breastfeeding, in combination with many broken nights, have sapped the energy of her mother. Using rhythm and uniformity, whether or not in combination with swaddling, it is generally easy to reduce the amount of breastfeading from ten to six sessions a day.

Do you recognize your child in these types and do you want to take action? We will return to these examples in the next chapter. As mentioned, there are two methods of turning the tide, one of which includes swaddling. Which of the two methods is most suitable for you will depend primarily on the age of your child, the type and duration of the problem, and the energy you still possess. In addition, there may be circumstances in which you should *not* swaddle your child (see Chapter 9).

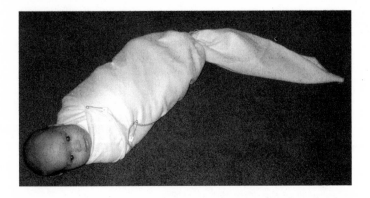

8. Taking stock of everyday activities

In order to discover where the problem lies, you need to investigate everyday activities. Gaining insight and understanding makes it easier to embark upon a new course. You may have been in a vicious circle for a while, associated with much emotion and feelings of powerlessness. The following issues may help you strip the daily routines of these emotions so that you can view the situation more clearly and objectively.

Your present situation holds the clues as to how best to turn the tide. Accordingly, the questions below try to clarify what has been done and what has not been done in the past week.

The questions:

A rough outline of the past week
On which days is the child at home and who is the carer?
On which day(s) is your child away from home, where and for how long?
How many outings does the child make every week and where does he go?
How many people come visiting every week?

A rough outline of one day at home
Is every day the same or is every day different?

The detailed time line from the beginning of one feed to the next feed, including the sleeping period
Take an inventory of the way that sleeping, playing and feeding have taken place, along with a description of the behaviour of your child and your reaction to this behaviour:

Sleep

How do you notice that your child is tired?

When do you lay your child down to sleep?

Where do you lay your child down to sleep?

Is your child awake or already asleep when you put
    him to bed?

Is your child allowed to cry for ten minutes before fall-
    ing asleep or for only a few seconds?

What clothes does your child wear in bed?

What is the temperature in the bedroom?

Is the room well ventilated?

Is the window open a little at night?

What do you use to cover your child?

Are the blankets loose on the bed or are they tucked in?

Is your child covered to the chest, to the shoulders, or
    to the neck?

How does the child fall asleep?

Does your child stay under the blankets or does he
    thrash around until he is uncovered?

Do you find him lying properly or lying across his
    bed?

How long does your child sleep?

How does your child wake up: refreshed, cheerful, cry-
    ing or whining?

Are the arms and hands warm or cold, pink or blue,
    when he wakes up?

What do you do when he wakes up?

Feeding

When does the child eat:

✿ just before, just after his sleep?

✿ at a random moment?

✿ when your child wants to?

How does your child eat: eagerly, greedily, slowly, with
   many breaks, easily distracted?
Does your child drink a complete 'meal' or a little bit
   in stages?
How long does the feeding last?
Does your child fall asleep during feeding?
What is the behaviour of your child during/after the feed:
   contented, crying, whining, irritated, complaining,
   throwing up?

Breastfeeding

Are you confident that your child is getting enough?
Do you give one or two breasts each time, with or
   without a break?
How many times a day?
How many times a night?
As comfort? To help him fall asleep?

Bottle-feeding

Which formula does your child receive?
Does your child get the prescribed amount?
How many bottles a day?

Playing

When do you play with your child/pay him attention?
Can your child amuse himself? For how long? Where?
   With what?
Does your child like to be entertained? For how long?
   By whom? Where? With what?
Are playthings out of reach, which you set in motion?
   How often? When? Where?

Is your child's game calm or does it become increasingly active as time goes on?

Crying

When does your child cry?
What kind of sound is that crying?
How does your child behave during this crying?
How many hours a day/night?
What do you do and how does your child react to this?

Growth

Is your child's growth under, above, or perfectly average? (Up to the age of three months a child will gain 100 to 300 grams a week.)

After answering these questions you will have a reasonably clear picture of your situation. Do you recognize your child in one of the John, Jim or Elizabeth models? Have you gained insight into the degree of (over-)tiredness, the extent of his ability to cope, and the amount of rhythm and uniformity in the life of your child? To what extent do your answers deviate from the 'fixed sequence of events' described earlier in this book? And from the uniformity? In assessing your current situation, bear in mind the information contained in Part 1 about ideal sleeping and feeding routines.

9. When to use which method

This chapter explains in detail when you should and when you should not apply the outlined methods. After reading this chapter, you will have sufficient information to make the appropriate intervention for you and your child.

Before using one of these methods you should ascertain whether or not your child is hungry. Could hunger be causing his restlessness and irregular sleeping and feeding patterns? This chapter explains the reasons for using or not using a particular method, but starts with the difference between *hunger* and *hunger for more.*

Hunger

A baby under six weeks old who is crying because he is hungry should obviously not be put to sleep crying. Especially when swaddled, such a young child could easily fall asleep despite its hunger, because he is too weak to protest — in fact, he may even fall asleep without swaddling. The child could become dehydrated if he is regularly put to bed hungry. If you suspect that your child's restlessness, crying, and irregular feeding and sleeping patterns are caused by hunger, try to discover whether this is really the case. This is more difficult if you breastfeed. You could weigh your child, fully-clothed, before and after feeding, using special baby scales. The difference in weight is the amount of breast milk your child has drunk. Don't change your child before you weigh him the second time. Write down the weight before and after feeding, leaving as little room for doubt as possible.

As a general rule, your child needs about 15 percent of his weight in milk every twenty-four hours. A breastfed child doesn't drink the same amount each time, but the balance should be the same as for a bottle-fed child — just so long as your child is satisfied when he releases the nipple. If he is not, it may be that your milk supply is low at that moment. Re-read the sections on 'Restlessness at the breast' and 'Too little milk' in Chapter 5 (p. 67) in order to determine a possible cause. When in doubt, consult the district nurse or an organization for breastfeeding mothers. With a little help, the dip in milk supply can usually be remedied and with that, the problem of restlessness.

Hunger for more

Many exhausted children appear insatiable in all respects. Each new stimulus is intriguing and satisfying, but for an increasingly brief moment. Then a new stimulus is required. Parents' creativity is unbelievable. I met a mother once who bounced around on a skippy ball with her child in her lap.

Some children appear to digest in the same fleeting manner. Each change in bottle-feeding causes considerable satisfaction — the parents sigh with relief — and the situation backfires after a day or three. Another new formula results in the same pattern. The restlessness and so-called sucking need are wrongly explained as hunger, while the underlying fatigue is not recognized. I have seen several 'crying babies' who were breastfed for the first two weeks of their lives, followed in rapid succession by various types of bottle-feeding: formula for hungry babies, for babies spitting up their feed, for babies with cramps ... The huge variety available in supermarkets is quite tempting, but unfortunately a change in this area rarely seems to solve the problem. A regular milk formula or breast milk, in amounts appropriate for the baby's age, turn out to be just fine once the fatigue is remedied. Even hypoallergenic formula usually proves to be unnecessary. Looking back after the problem has been solved, the many changes in bottle-feeding have often been illusory solutions. Exaggerated sucking and a fierce sucking response to a pacifier (dummy), breast or bottle were explained as a sign of hunger, but proved to be a sign of fatigue. Instead of hunger, the baby really needed a lot of sleep. What a pity for so many breastfed children whose mother unnecessarily switched to the bottle.

Don't experiment with different types of milk formula without consulting an expert.

Indications: when to intervene

There are no situations in which the introduction of *rhythm* and *uniformity* in your approach of your child is inappropriate, nor are there any special circumstances in which this intervention requires careful assessment.

Swaddling, however, can sometimes be inappropriate and should be considered carefully.

Both methods — that is, rhythm and uniformity, *and* swaddling — can be useful in the following situations:

1. Irregular sleeping and feeding patterns
Some children handle irregularity well, others don't. They have 30-minute catnaps and demand attention as soon as they wake up, crying and whimpering. They are unable to

fall asleep again to make up for their lack of sleep. Their irregular sleeping pattern usually precludes any rhythm in their feeding pattern. They usually drink little bits. They fall asleep at the breast or bottle out of sheer exhaustion before they are full. They wake up too soon because they get hungry again. Fatigue makes them irritable, which causes them to drink in a slapdash manner. They need to be fed much more often to satisfy their hunger. A vicious circle is established.

2. *An inability to fall asleep on his own and/or staying awake or waking himself up due to flailing arms.*

An inability to fall asleep on his own is often related to a habit of putting him to bed when he is already asleep. As you have read in 'Newborns up to six weeks old' (p. 23) many children who become used to this pattern in the first four weeks of their lives will be unable to fall asleep on their own. They will start to cry when they are put to bed and will increasingly flail their arms. Six to ten-week-old children who are still put to bed asleep will wake up within half an hour. They first become restless, as if they suddenly realize they are no longer in their parents' arms. Their jerking arms wake them up and they start to cry. A pattern may develop in which they hardly sleep for two days and then sleep all the time on the third day, just to survive. By the time they are three months old, they will be awake all day but sleep all night, again in order to survive. The parents may find this an ideal situation, experiencing a sense of freedom because their child doesn't need any naps during the day, but it will totally exhaust the child. Its greatly praised 'inquisitiveness and alertness' are nothing but an expression of fatigue.

These children's lack of sleep may result in:
* an inability to be or play by themselves
* a strong desire to be carried around or to be near the parent
* lots of whining and crying
* restless, irritable, overactive behaviour

3. Cramps

Colic or cramps occur frequently over the first three months of an infant's life. It is a normal phenomenon, because the intestines have not fully developed yet. Cramps can be a reaction to heavy foods eaten by the breastfeeding mother, including chocolate, and full grains such as rye, barley, wheat, muesli and breakfast products, rye bread, wholemeal bread, kidney beans, onions and leeks. They could also be caused by a cow's milk protein allergy, although this phenomenon occurs in a mere 2–5 percent of all crying babies. In order to rule out these causes, I recommend a visit to the health centre. Digestion is not often an obvious cause of cramps, however. The cause could be a combination of factors, including exhaustion and dealing with too many stimuli on the senses. Experience has shown that the use of the methods described in this book can considerably reduce these unexplained cramps.

Swaddling can be helpful when newborns show restless feeding behaviour

For some reason, some children are unable to master the feeding technique. Breast-, bottle- and/or child-related factors may play a role. Some high-spirited children simply don't have the patience to wait for the milk to come in, and start to shake their head violently. Swaddled as a compact package — you can also wrap the head in this case — he will lie still and won't be able to push himself away. As a result, the nipple or teat will stay in his mouth and he will drink more effectively. This has a double effect when you breastfeed: with a calmer child who latches on much better, your milk will arrive more quickly, which will make your child less impatient. Drinking will no longer be a problem. Both bottle- and breastfed children who drink calmly take in less air, which will result in less trouble with burps, cramps and posseting (spitting up).

Swaddling while you breastfeed won't be necessary for much more than a few days. Remove the cloths after feeding, and put your baby to sleep without cloths. Once the feeding problem is solved, it is best to refrain from swaddling altogether.

Contraindications — when not to swaddle

1. Hip dysplasia

The regular development of the hips is described in Chapter 11, 'Hip development and swaddling' (p. 126).

If your child suffers, or has suffered, from hip dysplasia, or if your physician suspects hip dysplasia, swaddling is not advisable. You should wait for the results of further tests. But even after your child has been successfully treated for hip dysplasia, it is better not to swaddle him. If a child with hip dysplasia makes jerking movements with his arms, resulting in a lack of sleep, he may be swaddled on the upper body and arms to limit the wild movements. Secure the cloth with at least two safety pins, and make sure it can't roll up to his face.

2. In cases of fever

Children with a fever need to get rid of the heat. Swaddling will slow this process down.

3. The first twenty-four hours after a DTP, HIB or other vaccination

This is because a fever might develop as a reaction to the vaccination.

4. In cases of serious infections of the respiratory system

Your child will need to cough, and a good cough sometimes requires use of the arms to make an extra effort. A regular cold is no reason to refrain from swaddling, though.

Special circumstances

Under special circumstances, such as posseting (spitting up) or eczema, swaddling may be an option, but not always. Consult your physician or health-centre doctor first. Special circumstances include:

1. Children with neurological problems

No general rules can be given for neurological problems because they are so diverse. Since these children are usually treated by a paediatrician or a physical therapist, it is best to consult them first when you think swaddling could be helpful.

2. Premature infants and infants with a low birth-weight

These children are often jumpy and cry more than full-term babies. They calm down considerably, and become less jumpy, when they are loosely wrapped in a closely woven cloth. Their arms and legs remain in the natural foetal position.

Wrapping is not the same as swaddling. In the hospital, under the supervision of the nurses, a wrapped baby can be put to sleep on its side. At home he may also be put to sleep in a wrap, but only on his back. Make sure the wrap can't roll up across the face, and secure it in several places with safety pins. If the child stays restless, you might want to switch to swaddling after all.

3. Children with a preferred position

A child with a preferred position is characterized by an asymmetrical position of the whole body, i.e., not just the head. The child is bent from head to toes in the so-called comma position. He prefers to look in one direction. When awake, he needs stimulation to assume a symmetrical position and to reach a symmetrical movement pattern. These children often need physiotherapy, so you should consult with the therapist whether you can swaddle. Hip dysplasia occurs more often in children with a preferred position. When in doubt about this, never swaddle.

A head flattened on one side, caused by your child's preference to sleep on that side, is not the same as the preferred position described here. A flattened head does not constitute a reason not to swaddle.

4. Children with eczema

Eczema can cause restlessness and a lack of sleep because a child is itching and wants to scratch himself. Swaddling makes this impossible, so the child gets to sleep again and the eczema settles down. It is not just the more relaxed sleeping but the experience of boundaries which has a healing effect on eczema. Experience has shown that swaddling can be used for dry eczema but not for wet eczema. Ask your doctor whether swaddling could be helpful for your child's type of eczema.

5. Posseting (Spitting up)

Posseting can take a large number of forms — a whole flood, little mouthfuls, all through the day, only during feeding or just after. Sometimes the feed is regurgitated and swallowed again. Posseting is often quite harmless — just one of those things that comes with your child. There is little you can do about it.

When spitting up is caused by restlessness, swaddling can be helpful. Make sure that a child who is spitting up, or even vomiting, is able to turn his head to the side. Always consult your doctor before you decide to swaddle.

The right method for your child

If swaddling is contraindicated, the introduction of rhythm and uniformity combined with swaddling is not an option for you. If there is no contraindication for swaddling, you can use both methods. The best method depends primarily on your child's age, the type and duration of the problem, and how much you can endure.

Regularity and uniformity without swaddling

If your child is less than ten to twelve weeks old, this method can be quite successful. Why? There are three main reasons:

1. A younger child does not have as much strength to protest for very long.

   The child is often so exhausted that he has no strength left to object to the new policy. After some protest when he is put to bed while still awake (which is a condition for both methods) sleep will prevail over the protest. Once the child manages to fall asleep on his own, the vicious circle is broken and a change is possible. Within a few days, your child will sleep longer, be more rested and accept the new routine.

2. A younger child has not developed the negative habit for too long. The shorter an undesired habit exists, the quicker it can be discarded.

3. A younger child does not have as much strength to undo its blankets. A tightly-made bed with a tightly tucked-in blanket (feet against the footboard and the blanket up to the chin) has a function similar to swaddling. The advantages of a tightly made bed are that:

✿ moving arms and legs isn't easy, so the child won't keep himself awake for so long

✿ the experience of limits, under the pressure of the tight blanket, gives him a sense of security

✿ warmth will spread through your child's body more evenly and he won't get cold hands easily (if properly dressed, of course)

Regularity and uniformity with *swaddling*

The added value of swaddling can be that:
✿ it prevents flailing arms and legs

✿ in addition to the constraints imposed by blankets, the
   swaddling cloths constitute an extra firm limit
✿ it offers a stronger sense of limitation, which gives
   your child a stronger sense of security
✿ swaddled children are more evenly warm

A tightly-made bed

It is hard to say which method is the most desirable. Each
situation, child and parent is different. For more on this
topic, see Chapter 14, 'Questions and answers' (p. 171).

Can parents use both methods without professional supervision?

The supervision required for the use of these methods
depends on the duration and seriousness of restlessness and
crying. It is hard to change patterns without any support.
When you are used to picking up your child every time
he cries or threatens to cry, it is not easy to stick to your
resolution not to pick him up immediately. Some women
ask a friend over for the first day, to lend support. Talking
through the daily routine with an outsider can work like a
mirror (see Chapter 8, p. 89). Once you understand how
a certain pattern can develop, it is less difficult to change
your own behaviour. Understanding it can give you the
motivation you need to use (one of) these methods and will
enhance your chances of success.

If you want to swaddle your child, I advise that you
discuss it with a health professional, who can determine
whether there are any reasons you shouldn't. He or she can
look over your shoulder to establish whether swaddling is
the right way to tackle the problem.

You're stronger in a team:

'My child was nine weeks old when I started swaddling. She screamed the house down, it broke my heart. She cried so loudly that I began to feel embarrassed, what with the neighbours sitting in their garden. So I picked her up. The next day my mother came over. You're stronger in a team. I swaddled her again. Giulia cried loudly for ten minutes, then stopped for a few minutes, started crying for about ten minutes again and fell asleep for four hours. We didn't know what was happening ...'

Lara, 6 weeks old:

'Lara cried a lot ever since she was born. When she was two weeks old, she didn't sleep for more than six hours out of twenty-four, and she was unable to fall asleep on her own, but we could still handle it. We devised our own little tricks. Still, her crying soon became unbearable.

There came a point where she was never satisfied. She didn't sleep at night, the sling didn't help. She even continued to cry when we tried to walk her to sleep. Falling asleep became a struggle. She cried all day and all night — twenty-four non-stop baby hours. It drove me crazy. That time of bliss everyone's talking about turned out to be pretty bleak. You become unsure, irritable, and depressed.

When the district nurse showed me how to swaddle Lara, at six weeks, I felt sorry for my poor baby, all wrapped up like a mummy.

Swaddling didn't help immediately. It took several days. We planned nothing for five whole days: no visitors, no outings, no telephone, only short walks, etc. We determined in advance how long we would let Lara cry. But after the first time we never had to pick her up again, because she settled down at intervals. We were often waiting at the bottom of the stairs to get her, but just as we would want to go up, she would go quiet.

Swaddling gave us a very satisfied little girl. The contact between us has become more intense, we really trust each other. We are better attuned to each other, she isn't as jumpy as she was and we can play with her and do things together just because she is rested. The contact between us is restored. She can fall asleep on her own now, because she feels safe and doesn't wave her arms and legs about as much as she used to. In short: the time of bliss has come after all.

The three Rs of Rest, Rhythm and Regulation are important for Lara. The room shouldn't be too lively, I myself shouldn't be too lively. The world can be so big and scary to a baby. It is so important to provide boundaries.'

10. Getting the routine right — the rules

The various steps toward change are the same for both methods: the introduction of regularity combined with swaddling, or the introduction of regularity without swaddling. This chapter will discuss the introduction of regularity and uniformity combined *with* swaddling. Should you decide not to swaddle, simply leave out the descriptions of swaddling and removing the cloths.

In addition to swaddling, introduce
strict rhythm and uniformity!

Strict rhythm and uniformity result in predictability. Your child will know what he can expect and will feel secure. This is the key to success. If either rhythm or uniformity is not introduced, your chances of success are slight.

It is particularly important that the places where your child is on his own and where he sleeps are always the same. This does not necessary apply to the places where you wash, change or feed your little one.

Rhythm and uniformity generally means that events of the day and their particular order become predictable — we know from experience what happens at one time and what comes next. There are no unexpected events to surprise or shock us. This allows us to relax. We don't have to be alert all the time. When you go through the same routine every day, your child will know that his first yawns are followed by bed and that bed is the place where he sleeps — because that's what happens every time he is put there! This uniformity of events allows your child to let go and surrender to sleep more easily. He will need less and less time to fall asleep on his own. His life is predictable, he feels secure.

If you let your actions depend on the situation, there is no predictability whatsoever.

Against the backdrop of these basic principles, three key aspects of the routine should be further explained:

1. Sleeping — waking up, then removing the cloths — feeding
2. Cuddling as much as needed, in your arms or on your lap — being alone/playing by himself in the playpen
3. First signs of weariness followed by swaddling and bed, while your baby is still awake

1. Sleeping — waking up, then removing the cloths — feeding

In the course of nature, waking up is followed by feeding. Children thrive on it. Getting a clean nappy in the mean-time does not disturb the sequence of events, because that is done very quickly. In addition to this natural need, there are other reasons for feeding immediately after waking up:

From small to large

The natural way is for things to move from small to large. This means that after waking up in his cot, the child is nursed in your arms or on your lap, or an older child sits in his bouncer or seat. This is followed by the bigger world of the playpen, or, for a toddler, the even bigger world of the room. In this way, the natural transition from small to large is reflected in the transition from sleep to wakefulness.

Playing takes energy, food gives energy

A child who has just woken up usually eats better when he has not yet been distracted. If you let your child play first, he could be too tired to eat well and may fall asleep during a feed. If you bottle-feed, you will be left with a part of the prescribed amount; if you breastfeed, you may not even notice that your child didn't drink enough. However, if you then put your child to bed while already asleep, he will wake up too soon because he is hungry again. The result of this pattern is often that the child will need smaller feeds more often and will take short naps. He will initially get enough in terms of nutrition, but not in terms of sleep. In the end the pattern of feeding and sleeping will become increasingly chaotic.

If you allow your baby to play before feeding when he is more than three months old, he will take new energy from food even though playing has made him tired. He will apparently overcome his sleep and become active again. As a result, his real tiredness will not be recognized.

You probably know this phenomenon from your own experience. Speaking for myself, a cracker and cheese late at night give me the energy to go on for another hour or two, busying myself with little things although I was really very tired and on my way to bed.

If sleep is delayed for too long, your child may become too tired to fall asleep on his own — falling asleep, as you know, requires a certain degree of 'surrender' and relaxation. The delay causes your child to miss out on a bit of sleep every day. He might get used to it, but it is not good for him.

100% sleep plus 100% feed gives 100% energy

Your child's basic needs are fulfilled when he has slept well and fed well. He will be totally ready for an active phase before it is time for bed again. After a healthy dose of cuddling he is ready to discover the wonders of his small world — on his own, keeping himself occupied.

Your child's body language will tell you when it is time for bed again. He is tired but satisfied. He will not exceed his limits of tiredness if you pick him up at the first signs of weariness and put him to bed. He will fall asleep on his own, wake up only when he becomes hungry, and then the whole cycle starts again from the beginning. The part where your child is on his own, exploring and amusing himself, is essential.

The older your child gets, the longer he will be able to stay awake, while he will sleep the same amount of time. This means that the amounts of time between feeds will increase, which means that there will be fewer feeds per day. If you breastfeed, you don't even have to think about this. If you bottle-feed, you simply stick to the instructions given for the age and weight of your child, dividing the stated amounts by the number of bottles you give each day.

2. Cuddling as much as needed, in your arms or on your lap (implicit attention) — being alone/playing alone in the playpen

Cuddling as much as needed, in your arms or on your lap
The amount of time you play with your child should be in proportion to the amount of time your child plays by himself. The older your child gets, the more time you can devote to him without impinging on the time he needs to be by himself. As long as your child can't be awake for more than one hour, including a feed (i.e., the first two months) the time you spend and play together can coincide with feeding. You will need about forty-five minutes for this,

which leaves another fifteen minutes for your child to play alone. I like to call this 'implicit attention:' when you pick up your child and busy yourself changing and bathing him, cuddling and play are performed naturally. You don't have to do anything special and it hardly takes any extra time.

Your implicit attention could include picking up your child in your arms, naturally followed by a greeting, a wide smile, cooing and talking to him, maintaining eye contact while you change him, combined with naming the parts of the body 'this is your tummy, and those are your toes ...' Children who are used to implicit attention are totally satisfied with this little ritual, and so are the parents. The parents have their hands free for household chores or a little time for themselves. The child, who has plenty of energy left, gets time to play by himself or enjoys looking at you doing whatever you are doing.

Don't play too long with your baby or he will get too tired. This is often not noticeable, because he responds enthusiastically and gets fresh energy from the contact with you. As soon as you put him in his playpen after this time together, however, he could get fussy. This behaviour is often interpreted as a rejection of the playpen or as boredom, and more attention to the child is a common reaction. In reality, though, he is simply tired and wants to sleep.

Being/playing alone without entertainment, preferably in the playpen

Your child finds it quite natural that the usual routine of feeding, changing and cuddling is followed by some time alone. Once again, uniformity is the magic word: one thing is always followed by the next — feeding is followed by a nappy (diaper) change, which is followed by cuddling, which is followed by being or playing by himself. Satisfied in all respects, your child will explore his small world in his own way. He will be able to play by himself until he gets tired and is ready for bed again, which he will show you in his own way.

Although a baby can't really play at six weeks, he can definitely be by himself for a while. Touching, hearing and smelling the surrounding world and atmosphere — the less distraction he gets, the more focused he will be. A child who can smile starts to play by himself when he seeks contact with the environment, which at that time includes his own body and clothes.

It is essential that your child understands, because of the uniformity of your behaviour, when it is time to be by himself and amuse himself. The pen plays an important role here, since it will be recognized by your child as the place where the routine continues. If you don't use a playpen, this fixed point is absent and you will have to indicate by your behaviour that it is time to play, which is much more difficult than using a playpen. Without realizing it, you will vary the place where you put your child to be by himself, which will disrupt the predictability you were aiming for. You child does not recognize the uniformity and becomes alert and curious because of the ever changing environment. Any latent weariness will not be recognized. Another advantage of the playpen is that it offers a tangible boundary between you and your child. This will make it easier to break with any old behavioural patterns you might have developed.

The playpen as a prison or convenient dumping place: a misunderstanding

For children up to one year old, the playpen is a safe, manageable place to play. Within its boundaries, they can explore the world on their own and enjoy the freedom they have. It would be wrong, therefore, to consider the playpen as a limitation of freedom. When the playpen becomes the regular place for being by himself, your baby will be totally satisfied with that. Children who are used to the playpen are content to play in their own defined corner until they are as much as three years old. Leaving your child in the playpen does not mean that there should be no contact with your child — on the contrary. Do by all means react to his noises or stroke his head when you walk by. This is a healthy form of communication which does not interrupt the child's play. It would be different if you were to sit next to the playpen and keep the game going, preventing your child from playing by himself. You should obviously offer playthings which suit the age of your child. A child who begins to crawl could in addition be given the opportunity — for instance, once a day — within the predictable order of events, to explore the big world of the floor.

A child who knows that the time spent together with you is followed by some time by himself in the playpen will play until he gets tired. No more, no less — that is as long as there is not a plaything that fascinates him too much. This could be the case with a mobile over the playpen, which you put in motion continuously. This continues to draw your child's attention and wears him out. Instead of yawning, whining or crying, he may get increasingly lively.

3. First signs of weariness followed by swaddling and bed, while your baby is still awake

Why put a child to bed upon the first signs of weariness?
Because it meets the natural needs of your child and prevents exhaustion. It is not good for any child to exceed the limits

of tiredness. It is difficult for an exhausted child to surrender to sleep. This might sound a bit odd. Many parents whose children don't sleep much allow them to get extra tired in the hope that they will sleep. What they get is the opposite.

Why put the child to bed awake?

Children who are used to being put to bed awake recognize the bed as a familiar place where they are allowed to sleep. Having shown signs of tiredness, they will be quite happy and satisfied to be put to bed and will easily surrender to sleep. They sometimes babble a bit to themselves before they fall asleep, and when they wake up again, they look around a bit before indicating that it is time for a meal. Waking up, they recognize their bed as a familiar and safe place. Children who cannot fall asleep on their own sometimes can't play by themselves either. These are the children who demand more entertainment, get it and sleep less and less.

> The ability to fall asleep on his own is a precondition for breaking through a pattern of dependence.

When is the best time to start?

It is important that you, your partner and your child spend several consecutive days (or a week, if possible) at home when you want to start with the method of swaddling and the introduction of rhythm and uniformity. The familiar environment offers tranquillity and security for becoming accustomed to the new routine. Rhythm and uniformity are easier to introduce in the familiar environment of home. If the child spends one day at home and the next in day-care, the chances of success are much smaller. In that case it would be best to start immediately before a quiet weekend. Try not to interrupt the new routine unnecessarily with shopping, long walks or visits. The big changes in your child, as a result of swaddling and the new routine, will allow you to recognize your child's real needs more easily. Your life will really change. A new sleeping pattern will emerge after one to two weeks. You will then be able to fit in your household tasks efficiently, as well as your social life. When you go out walking your child can sleep in the pram, swaddled snugly. When you return, leave him in the pram until his next feed. If necessary, turn back the blanket to prevent him from getting too hot. Swaddling and the new routine can then be trusted to other carers if you wish.

The following rules are the keys to success

a. Make sure you are motivated, so that you won't give up when you are halfway through.

b. Make sure you are fully informed.

c. Swaddle your child upon the first signs of weariness and put him to bed awake.

d. Accept the fact that your child may cry before he falls asleep in the transitional phase to the new routine, and always respond in the same way.

e. Feed your child as soon as he wakes up.

f. Swaddle for any odd nap, making sure that the cloths become a familiar part of sleep.

g. Continue to swaddle for at least six weeks after a stable rhythm has developed.

h. Gradually reduce swaddling.

The above eight rules concern behaviour. The next two are about the way the bed is made and what your child should wear in bed.

i. Provide boundaries with a properly made bed.

j. Dress him in comfortably warm, but not too warm clothes to sleep in — try to find something just right.

More detailed explanation of the rules

a. Make sure you are motivated, so that you won't give up when you are halfway through.

Take the bull by the horns, and do it now. Stick to your decision and persevere on the course you have chosen. Let go of your old behavioural patterns. Don't falter or you will fail to create uniformity, both for yourself and your little one. Besides, doing half the job is rarely effective, even when you achieve some results in the beginning. You may be thrilled to find that your child sleeps 20 percent more, while experience shows that he could sleep up to 50 percent more if you were to stick to your new approach.

b. Make sure you are fully informed.

In order to avoid mistakes and to make sure you know how to swaddle properly, absorb as much information as you can. Try to understand the reasons for the approaches I am describing in this book. Make them your own, so that you make the decision with heart and mind to do it this way and not any other way. Moreover, swaddling in combination with rhythm and uniformity produces the desired results more quickly when you follow the instructions. Pick up this book from time to time, to check whether you are still doing it 'according to the book.' You might overlook certain important things once a routine has established itself. For instance, when your child has outgrown his cot, is his new bed in harmony with the guidelines?

c. Swaddle your child upon the first signs of weariness and put him to bed awake.
Signs of weariness include:

✿ yawning
✿ pallor
✿ rubbing the eyes
✿ whining
✿ becoming more lively
✿ breaking off eye-contact and looking away

A child who is used to being put to bed awake upon the first signs of tiredness will sleep as much as he needs. If you respond to his signs, you fulfil his natural needs. Picking him up as soon as he indicated that he is tired, and putting him to bed means 'I am now allowed to sleep.' Your child will soon recognize this regular rule.

If it is difficult to recognize the signs of tiredness in an infant, start by putting him to bed after an hour. At three to six weeks old, children generally manage to stay awake for forty-five minutes including feeding, so this slightly exceeds the limit. After a few days, your child will be more rested and any signs of tiredness will be easier to recognize.

Most children who need to be swaddled are not used to being put to bed while they are still awake. Looking back, parents often find that putting their child to bed after he had already fallen asleep in their arms caused the whole problem.

d. Accept the fact that your child may cry before he falls asleep in the transitional phase to the new routine, and always respond in the same way. Use a kitchen timer!

Crying in this transitional phase is nothing but a healthy protest against the new, strange course of action. It is simply a part of it. The more consistent you are, the sooner you will reap the benefits of your new approach. Your own and your child's efforts will be substantially rewarded. There is plenty of evidence to support this. Many children need to cry themselves to sleep. It is their way of letting go. You may not know this of your child, since you were used to picking him up when he cried. Decide how long you will allow your child to cry. You could set the kitchen timer for thirty minutes after putting your child to bed. This helps you keep a realistic sense of time. You allow your child to overcome his resistance by himself, to let go and give in to sleep. Find something to keep yourself busy in the meantime. This can make it easier for you to get through this wait.

Depending on his age, your child may object fiercely the first time. Listen carefully to how he cries. Experience has shown that many children cry their hearts out for fifteen minutes, then go quiet for a few seconds. They need some air. I advise you to reset the kitchen timer for another thirty minutes in that intermission, to give both your child and yourself some more time. After this, the duration and intensity of crying usually diminishes, and the breathers become longer. This can easily take half an hour. After that you may experience a moment of anxiety because your child will appear to start screaming again but then, all of a sudden, he will go quiet. Your child sleeps! Should you worry about your child's well-being, take a peek without being seen yourself. You will probably find a contentedly sleeping baby. If you manage to get through this first crying session, you have achieved a great deal. Your child learns quickly. The second time round he will probably cry for less than ten minutes.

e. Feed your child as soon as he wakes up

Doing this means that you are focused on fulfilling his natural needs. In the new approach, waking up and being picked up means 'I am now allowed to eat.' Your child will soon recognize this regular pattern. It may require some effort when you were used to feeding your child before putting him to bed. A child who has slept well and is subsequently fed well is a happy child. It will not be hard for you to notice the first signs of tiredness: it's time for bed again!

f. Swaddle for any odd nap

In the same way, swaddling will become part of the routine for both you and your child. On seeing the swaddling cloths before being put to bed, your child knows: 'I am allowed to sleep again.' You offer him no routine if you only swaddle at difficult times.

g. Continue to swaddle for at least six weeks

Once a stable rhythm has developed, it takes at least six weeks before the new behavioural pattern has really sunk in.

h. Gradually reduce swaddling

When you have taken one or two weeks to break through the old behavioural pattern and develop a new one, you can try to reduce swaddling again after six more weeks. I know from experience that children generally need swaddling for three months. The way to reduce swaddling is described in Chapter 13.

Rules for making the bed and sleeping clothes

In addition to the behavioural rules, there are two important rules where the bed is concerned. Chapter 12 offers more information about this, particularly with regard to the sense of security. Chapter 2 also mentions the topic under the developmental stage from 'Newborns up to six weeks old' (see p. 23).

i. Provide boundaries with a properly made bed

Firm definition gives a sense of security and limits the freedom of movement of the arms and legs. The child will fall asleep more easily and will sleep longer.

Make the bed so that your child's feet reach the footboard, and place the child on its back (see illustration p. 137). Use a sheet and blanket big enough to be properly tucked in under the mattress, so that the weight of the child keeps the blanket in place. Cover your child up to the chin with the shoulders well-covered. If your child is not swaddled, try to get his arms under the blanket. The younger the child, the easier this is.

j. Dress him in comfortably warm, but not too warm clothes, for sleeping — try to find something just right.

We all know that in order to sleep well, we must be comfortably warm. Use a fitted, non-padded sleeping bag. Make

sure that the sleeves of a sleeping bag, sleepsuit (footie) or
a pair of pyjamas are not too wide and that they reach the
hands (and not just somewhere below the elbow). Should
the hands get away from under the blanket, the warmth of
the arms will prevent them from cooling off too quickly.
Sleeves that are not too wide and fit snugly around the arms
contribute to the sense of boundary and limit the freedom
of movement.

Having given these tips, I rely on your common sense
and sound judgement. Bedclothes and sleeping clothes
should obviously be chosen in accordance with the envi-
ronmental temperature. Keep this and the tips in Chapter
12 in mind.

Making the bed

There is a persistent misunderstanding about making the
bed, as is currently recommended. Many people assume
that the child should only be covered up to the chest.
Several study books on child care even state this. I must
disagree. Making the bed in this way only causes problems.
The child gets very cold because nearly half of his body is
not covered. Lying on his back, the child is stretched out
and can easily overstretch when he gets a cramp or is subjected to external stimuli.

A properly tucked-in child falls asleep more easily,
sleeps better and longer. He will move less and feel secure
because of the sense of boundary, which will cause him to
be less easily disturbed in his sleep. As I described in Part 1
of this book, this is the way to put your child to bed, and is
an excellent measure against crying and restlessness.

Once restlessness has developed and the method of
rhythm and uniformity without swaddling is used, the

above-mentioned rules are very important. A child who is put to bed in this way is more or less 'swaddled' under his tightly tucked-in blanket, and basically the same principles apply.

In cases of rhythm and uniformity combined *with* swaddling, the tightly tucked-in blanket and the additional limitation of movement provide added value.

Two final tips

Don't aim for a tight schedule

When you introduce rhythm and uniformity, your child will develop its own pattern. A child older than three months generally sleeps longer and plays less in the morning than in the afternoon. In the afternoon he sleeps less and plays longer. The duration of one sequence may vary, but may also be more or less the same. Don't aim for a fixed schedule. It does work sometimes, but could go against the needs of your child. As long as your child is playing contentedly by himself, he shows that nobody is asking too much of him. There is no need to worry when he doesn't sleep as long in the afternoon. It will probably be impossible to get him to sleep any longer.

There may be family situations which force you to adjust the rhythm of your child to the rhythm of other family members. This is especially the case with twins. Nevertheless, I would strongly advise you to introduce the child to the new routine using rhythm and uniformity. Only when your child has caught up on his lack of sleep and is rested can small deviations be made. Generally speaking, it is alright to wake up your child before he wakes up spontaneously, provided that you feed him immediately. This is not advisable when your child is exhausted. Exhaustion, as we have seen above, has a severe impact on the quality of falling asleep and sleeping.

Don't force your child to sleep in the afternoon

After the description of the rules above, this should be obvious, but it still happens occasionally. Parents of a restless child with a sleeping problem are often not aware of the child's real sleeping requirements — which is quite understandable in their situation. One mother told me, for instance, that her three-month-old never used to sleep at all during the day, and that she only began to put him to bed for a nap in the afternoon when she started swaddling. And he slept! You will understand how happy she was with this afternoon gift. Those who know the result of properly introduced rhythm and uniformity will know that three-month-old children need much more sleep than just what they get during the night. An imposed afternoon nap, however, prevents a child from showing his real needs, and his parents will therefore not pick up the signs.

11. Practical swaddling

Preparations

Which swaddling cloths should you use? Which fabric is suitable, and how big should the cloths be? And what clothes should your baby wear underneath them?

Fabric

You can sew your own cloths or buy ready-made and finished cloths. There are beautiful blankets and complete swaddling sacks available.

In this book I suggest the use of two cloths or blankets. In more than nine years I've seen excellent results with this method. Occasional changes have been introduced but the method is essentially the same.

Use cotton material, preferably a thin flannel or muslin, which ensure that the cloths stay in place. You could use an old, slightly worn flannel sheet. The fabric should not be too hot, but needs to be firm enough to offer constraint. A cotton bed-sheet is too thin and too smooth. New flannel is nice and soft, but too hot, especially in the summer months. Don't use synthetic or elasticated fabrics. A regular diagonal stretch is alright and makes it even easier to wrap your baby. It is best, but not absolutely necessary, to finish the edges with a flat hem.

Dimensions

The method used in this book is based on sets of one square cloth plus an oblong cloth for the legs. The dimensions of the cloths should allow for a little growth. It is difficult to give exact dimensions. Some parents use thin flannel nappies for the first weeks of life. I think they are rather small — the child soon outgrows them and easily wriggles out of them, and besides, it is more difficult to get your child wrapped in small cloths. When you start swaddling, the cloths should be big enough, but not too big. The package simply gets too hot when the cloths are wrapped around the child more times than indicated in the illustrations. So don't buy or sew cloths twice the given size just because they offer room for growth. It is obvious that your child will outgrow them when you intend to swaddle for some time. Make the switch to a bigger size in good time.

The set described for a child aged four months and upward lasts much longer than the first two, because children of this age tend to grow in length rather than width.

THE DIMENSIONS OF THE OUTER CLOTH AND THE LEG CLOTH, RESPECTIVELY:

Set A — up to 6–8 weeks (approx. 5 kg):
  90 × 90 cm and 65 × 90 cm.

Set B — 6–8 weeks up to 4 months (approx. 6 kg):
  100 × 100 cm and 70 × 100 cm.

Set C — 4 months and up: 120 × 120 cm and 80 × 120 cm.

What should a child wear beneath the cloths?
Your baby should be neither under nor overdressed — not too cold, not too hot. Don't use synthetic fabrics, because they are cold and sweaty. Make sure your child is evenly warm, including his legs and feet. When his extremeties

are cold it means that the warmth is going to his head. Put another layer on the lower part of the body, or use a warmer leg cloth. A bodysuit followed by a cotton long-sleeved shirt and warm socks should do the trick. If your child fiercely protests at this stage — which could cause him to sweat a lot — dress him in nothing but a bodysuit. Your child's neck is always a good place to check whether he is warm enough.

Let's do it

Okay, let's get going. What is the best working posture for you, and what do you do when your child begins to cry while you are swaddling him? How do you give your child a little room to settle in his own way? How do you prevent him from rolling over on his tummy?

The swaddling technique is explained step by step, with clear illustrations (see pp. 128–135).

Posture

Work standing at the changing table or kneeling by your own bed. Lie your child in front of you with his feet pointing towards you. Stroke your child in order to make him relax. Your hands will move about while you are swaddling. Make sure you continue to touch your child whenever one of your hands is free. This will soothe him. Talking, singing or humming also helps you to maintain contact. Practise on a doll or teddy bear to develop some speed. You may be a bit clumsy at the start — don't worry, accept it with a smile. You don't have to start all over if the result isn't perfect. It would take you too long to get your child swaddled. Continue working even if your child is crying. Your child senses that you are taking charge. It will reassure him. As soon as you are finished pick him up and stroke his back confidently. If he is crying he will relax. If he becomes restless in bed, because he can wriggle an arm free at the neck, it means that the cloths are not wrapped properly.

Hip development and swaddling

Your child's hips are not fully grown at birth. The soft bones still contain a lot of cartilage. During the first six months of life especially the hip joint is shaped through the reciprocal pressure of the end of the thighbone and the socket of the hipbone. This is usually a natural process helped along by the child's movements and play. Playing on the flat floor of a playpen is much better than sitting in a baby bouncer or first-stage car seat. A sleeping child doesn't move much — or shouldn't. Movement is part of being awake. In order not to interfere with the natural development of the hips though, the legs of a child under six months old should have enough room to move. He should be able to stretch and bend his legs in the cloths.

Medical professionals check hip development regularly in the first year. Tell him or her at each visit that you swaddle your baby, and ask for his or her feedback.

Leg cloth

The inner leg cloth is not fixed; it is wrapped around the lower part of the body, from the elbow down. This gives your child some room to settle on his own. The arms are lightly fixed in this cloth, which makes wrapping the second cloth easier. The use of the leg cloth is important, particularly from the age of three months onward, because a child of this age gains more control over his own legs and increasingly enjoys kicking and moving. The use of the leg cloth prevents too wide movements of the legs, although there is enough room within the cloth to spread and stretch out the pulled-up legs. Look carefully at the natural position of your child when he lies awake without swaddling. Give him enough room to move like that within the leg cloth. The outer cloth should wrap your child into a snug package.

The outer cloth

This cloth wraps your child from the shoulders down to the feet. The remaining cloth is tied together with a piece of string or tape below the feet of the stretched-out legs. This prevents the cloths from rolling up and the legs from peeking out, causing a 'leak' for body heat and energy. Besides, a 'hole' disrupts the overall sensation.

It is safer to leave the remaining cloth in the bed like a tail. Never tuck it in under the mattress. Your child could get trapped in it when he rolls over. Swaddle the arms tightly, stretched out alongside the body. It is alright if the hands worm towards your baby's tummy, but don't bend the arms before you start or the swaddling could become too tight. Besides, this position gives your child so much strength in his elbows that he will start to wriggle and continue to wriggle, and swaddling would have an adverse effect.

Prevent rolling

At six months you need to swaddle the legs more tightly, or your child will be able to roll over on to his tummy. The chances of tight cloths interfering with hip development are minimal at this age.

Step by step swaddling

1. Fold the top of the square cloth. The folding line should be longer than the length of the outstretched arms of your child. If the cloth is a bit too big, fold the top further down. As you can see in Step 12 (p. 133), the very last tip should end up by the elbow/underarm. If you finish much lower, the fabric could become wrapped too tightly around the hips, which must never happen. Place the oblong (leg) cloth on top, about 10 cm from the folding line.

2. Place your child in the middle of his cloths, his shoulders about 4 cm below the folding line.

3. Stretch his left arm down next to his body and hold it in
   place with your left hand. Take up the leg cloth on the
   right side (*your* right side) and pull it across the chest
   to the left side. The part of the arm and chest above the
   elbow remains free. Tuck this part of the cloth under
   your child. Fold the lower part of the cloth in a diagonal line beneath your child, creating a skirt-like look.
   *With children older than six months, the cloth should be
   wrapped tightly from top to bottom.*

4. Do the same thing on the other side. Do not fix this
   side underneath your child's body, giving him some
   room to 'settle' in his own way. With a child up to six
   months old, make sure he can bend his legs and spread
   them from the hips. *Again, with children older than six
   months, the cloth is wrapped tightly from top to bottom.*

5. Now hold the underlying square cloth tight between your body and the edge of the bed or changing table to keep the cloth straight. With your left hand, hold the wrapped left arm in place next to the body. With your right hand, take the edge of the fold (see illustration below) and pull it slightly from under your child to his upper right. This will cause the lower point of the fold to move from beneath your child's back to the right, which gives you more fabric to fold this flap under the chin and across the chest to the right arm.

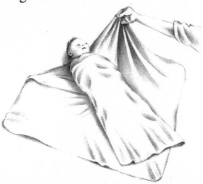

6. As before, hold the underlying cloth tight between your body and the edge of the bed or changing table to keep the cloth straight. Put your right hand across the chest, just below the chin. Your thumb points to your child's right foot, creating the line for folding

one corner of the cloth. To do this, take one edge of
the fabric as illustrated.

7. Guide the cloth along the line of your thumb across the
   chest to just below the wrapped right elbow. Take the
   fabric by the left edge and guide it upward until you
   feel it on your thumb. Now guide the tight fabric parallel to your index finger across the body to the left. The
   new folding line comes at the same height as the upper
   edge of the leg cloth.

8. Put your right hand on top of the layers of cloth to keep
   everything in place. Tuck the fabric under your child,
   giving the legs more room like a skirt. *With children
   older than six months, the cloth is wrapped tightly from
   top to bottom.*

9. Put your right hand on your child's chest. With your left hand, take the folded flap by the edge (see below). Pull it slightly up, just like you did with the other side and fold the cloth under the chin, across the chest, to the left arm. Don't make a collar.

10. Put your left hand across the chest, just below the chin. Your thumb points in the direction of your child's left foot. Once again, this is the line to fold away the cloth as shown below. To do this, take the cloth by the edge with your other hand.

11. Guide the cloth along the line of your thumb across the chest to just above the left wrapped elbow. This

works as follows: take the fabric by the right edge and guide it upward until you feel it on your thumb. Then guide the tightly held fabric parallel to your index finger across the body to the right. The new folding line is at the same height as the previous folding line.

12. Put one hand on the chest to keep the fabric in place. With the other hand, smooth the fabric down — it flares like a skirt. Take the last tip of the fabric in your right hand. Keep the fabric tight so that your child stays firmly wrapped. Bring the tip horizontally across the left elbow, under the back and to the front again past the right elbow/underarm. This last move finishes your work. Now fix the fabric at the level of the elbow/underarm with a safety pin.

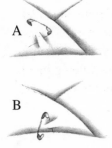

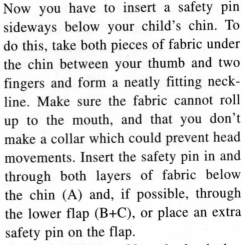

Now you have to insert a safety pin sideways below your child's chin. To do this, take both pieces of fabric under the chin between your thumb and two fingers and form a neatly fitting neckline. Make sure the fabric cannot roll up to the mouth, and that you don't make a collar which could prevent head movements. Insert the safety pin in and through both layers of fabric below the chin (A) and, if possible, through the lower flap (B+C), or place an extra safety pin on the flap.

There, you have firmly fixed the top. Now check whether the cloths offer enough room around the hips if your child is younger than six months. To do this, insert your arms in the leg cloths on both sides of the hips and legs, and create some more room.

Use a piece of string no longer than 30 cm to close off the cloths on the underside, some 5 cm past the stretched legs, or use a piece of tape. In this way you keep the remaining fabric together and you prevent the fabric from rolling up.

When your child is older than six months, wrap the fabric tightly around the child from hip to foot. Fix it with at least three safety pins.

Fixing the cloths

1. WITH SAFETY PINS

This is the method I prefer, particularly for children aged eight weeks and upward. When you stick them into a bar of soap before you start, they slide through the fabric more easily. Use the biggest size.

2. WITH MASKING TAPE

Strong masking tape can be tried for little ones in the first weeks of life. You will find out soon enough whether or not it keeps the fabric in place. Unlike a safety pin which fixes several layers of fabric, tape connects only two pieces.

If you find your child with loose or loosened cloths, you know it's time to switch to safety pins.

Never wrap the tape around your child. It could get caught or even cause breathing problems.

> *Loose swaddling is dangerous — avoid it!*

12. The bed and sleeping

Conditions for a safe and successful intervention

Although rhythm, uniformity and the swaddling itself are important, your child's bed, the temperature of his room, and your child's sleeping posture are also essential. What sort of bed is best? How do you make it and where should you put it?

The bed

Make sure the mattress is firm and level, and that it is not shorter or narrower than the bed by more than 2 cm. The hard bottom of the bed should offer enough ventilation. Don't use a sheepskin (in combination with swaddling) or pillow. Don't put a pillow-like cuddly toy or loose cloth in your child's bed. If you use a waterproof sheet, don't place it under your child's head. Being impermeable, these sheets can make the bed too hot and are best avoided when you swaddle your child. Use cotton (preferably 100 percent) sheets and a woollen or cotton blanket. Don't use an eiderdown, and don't put blankets in an eiderdown cover. Air the mattress regularly and check the underside for humidity spots.

Making the bed

Make the bed so that your child's feet reach the footboard. The blanket should come up to your baby's chin and should be tucked smoothly under the mattress on both sides. In this way, the baby's weight keeps the blanket neatly in place. Blankets are often too narrow to be tucked in properly. If this applies to your baby's blanket use it lengthways across the bed. Make sure the mattress stays

straight. If you don't tuck the blanket in evenly, you can create a pit in the middle.

Some children like to have their head at the head of the bed; when you come and get them for a feed, you will find that they have crept all the way up. If your child apparently needs a tangible boundary for his head, you can make the bed smaller, up to the age of eight weeks: use a regular oblong sheet as a bottom sheet, tuck it in at the head of the bed and fold it over halfway. The folded part is used as the top sheet. Cover it with a blanket — make sure it is wide enough — and fold the top of the sheet back over the blanket — make sure the flap is big enough. Then tuck in the sheet and blanket evenly. I advise against this method for stronger children older than eight weeks, because they are strong enough to wriggle toward the footboard, causing the sheet to come loose. This in turn creates a choking hazard. Never use pillows or a nursing pillow to 'reduce' a bed.

The position of the bed

Just like any other child, your swaddled child may get sick. In order for you to notice this in time, it is important to monitor him. If possible, let your baby sleep in your bedroom for the first six months — in his own bed, never in yours. Do make sure, however, that this proximity does not result in giving him more attention, and keep a 'loving distance.' During the day, place the bed in such a way that you can watch your child without him seeing you.

Bedroom temperature

The room temperature and the outside temperature also deserve your attention. Even in winter you should have a window ajar, and no, or as little, heating as possible in the bedroom. 15°C is warm enough (there are other guidelines for newborns up to six weeks old and for children with asthma). Give your child another layer of clothing and/or another blanket rather than turning up the heating. On hot summer days you can remove a few layers of clothing, or even swaddle your baby without any other clothes. Do try, however, to at least tuck in the sheet when it's hot. The pressure and immobilizing effect of the covers significantly enhance the impact of swaddling and ensure that your child gets used to sleeping covered more easily. Once you start reducing the swaddling, your child still experiences the familiar boundary of the tight blanket, which makes the transition to sleeping without swaddling easier.

Sleeping posture

Always put your child to sleep on his back. The side posture is unstable. Your child can easily roll over on his tummy, which is dangerous. Try to alternate the direction of the head. If your child has a preference for one side, try to turn his head while he is fast asleep, hoping he will stay like that. If your child turns to the light all the time, you could try to turn the bed.

Never put your swaddled child in your own bed or on a waterbed.

Sleeping face-down in relation to cot death

Ever since face-up became the recommended sleeping posture, the number of cot deaths has dropped considerably. The use of a sleeping bag is also recommended, because children change their sleeping posture less often in a sleeping bag. As you have read above, you should always put a swaddled child to sleep on his back. Swaddled children don't turn over easily, because their legs are wrapped. With a blanket and sheet (or just a sheet, depending on the bedroom temperature) tucked in tightly as described above, the child will stay on his back more securely, further reducing the risk of cot death. Swaddled children who do manage to turn over on their tummy are usually older than five or six months, and often have loose swaddling cloths on their legs, or their feet sticking out. Using their legs and feet, they manage to roll over like a little seal.

As I have said before, it is important to prevent a swaddled child from rolling over on his tummy.

Double-check that:

- ✿ your baby's feet don't stick out
- ✿ the cloths are tight enough around the legs (older than 6 months)
- ✿ your baby can't wriggle out an arm
- ✿ you have used a big enough blanket

- ✿ the blanket is properly done — just below the chin and tucked in smoothly
- ✿ the mattress fits properly so that the tucked-in blanket stays in place between the mattress and the bed

---

If your swaddled child continues to try and roll over on his tummy, *stop* swaddling!

Heat stasis in relation to cot death

Sleeping under an eiderdown can result in heat stasis. Many eiderdowns provide as much warmth as between four and seven blankets. An eiderdown increases the risk of cot death, especially if a baby's head ends up under it. This is why I strongly advise against eiderdowns in general, and for swaddled babies in particular. A swaddled child is unable to push away its eiderdown. A swaddled child should not be too hot — in fact, no child should be too hot. A crying swaddled baby whose head is bare can sweat a lot. Sweating is a healthy way to lose excessive heat. Children lose 60 percent of their body heat via the head. When the previous instructions on clothing and bed are followed, you don't have to worry about excessive heat. Some children are even put to sleep too cold for fear of heat stasis. They use up lots of precious energy to keep up their temperature, energy which cannot then be used for growth and development. Try to strike a happy medium and keep your baby comfortably warm.

13. From routine to a gradual discontinuation of swaddling

We have looked at the rules, the preconditions and the way to actually swaddle your baby. I shall now describe the process of introducing and maintaining rhythm and uniformity over several weeks, either combined with swaddling or not. The process is more or less the same in both cases.

A diary for guidance and as a frame of reference

A personal diary is quite useful for the first few weeks. It gives you a clear overview of what happens, where it happens and how long it takes or lasts. It also allows you to keep a grip on time, lessening the feeling that the day is slipping through your fingers. It works like a mirror and a reminder, and when there is visible progress, an encouragement.

Start by filling in any random day of the past week when you were not yet using the method. You should be able to roughly describe your initial situation. Use colours if you like — for example, yellow for the times your baby was awake, blue for the times he slept and red for the times he cried. This will give you an instant overview. You may be shocked by what you see: 'I didn't know it was that bad! Does my baby sleep so little? There is no rhythm whatsoever!'

Keeping track of everything that happens, you can see how much time you have to entertain your child and how long he can be by himself. You will soon notice a shift from him *being* entertained to playing contentedly by himself. You will also discover how outings and other unexpected events affect your child. Does he cry less and sleep more? Have you shown uniform behaviour? How many feeds did you give today? Did your bottle-fed child finish every bottle, or did he want more feeds or leave more leftovers? Your diary offers objective feedback, guidance and support.

	where	crying	whining	com-forting	feeding	playing together	playing alone	sleeping
07:00								
07:20								
07:40								
08:00								
08:20								
08:40								
09:00								
09:20								
09:40								
10:00								
10:20								
10:40								
11:00								
11:20								
11:40								
12:00								
etc. until 06:40								

Three phases from routine to reduction

The introduction of rhythm and uniformity, with or without swaddling, can be roughly divided into three phases:

First phase: routine, one to two weeks

With or without swaddling, your child may react to the new routine in several ways, ranging from resistance and crying, sweating profusely, to total submission. The third day often shows a relapse, followed by a period of getting used to the new rhythm and swaddling, and the development of a routine, which is restful for both the parents and the child.

Second phase: the new pattern sinks in

Take at least six weeks for this phase.

Third phase: reduction in swaddling

Depending on the child and the situation, you will either stop abruptly or gradually reduce the number of times you swaddle your baby. The newly acquired rhythm and uniformity are retained, of course.

Let's consider each phase in detail. The descriptions below assume the use of rhythm and uniformity, and swaddling. If you don't swaddle, you can generally replace the term 'swaddling' with 'putting to sleep awake, under a tightly tucked-in blanket (depending on the bedroom temperature).'

The first phase: routine, one to two weeks

The first few days are the hardest. Depending on the situation, you have to deal with different aspects and questions. For instance, what to do when your child resists, and for how long should you let your baby cry? What is the 'dip' like, and what do you do when your child has no problems falling asleep but wakes up too soon?

It is difficult to discard old habits. This applies to every parent. However, most parents of restless children are relieved to find that they have a concrete and consistent approach to work with.

Use the rules I described in Chapter 10 as a guideline. Try to follow them as closely as you can in your interaction with your child. Your diary will show how well you are succeeding and how much progress you are making. With some children, parents manage to go by the book right from the start. These children adjust to the new routine and hardly resist at all. Other children need more time to accept the routine, and require a few extra steps and a less direct path to victory.

The first thing you need is a turning point in the downward spiral of fatigue. You have achieved this as soon as your child has slept well for a few hours, once or twice a day. He will feel so much better that he will be able to eat as soon as he wakes up, in accordance with the new routine, *and* will eat better, and may even be content to play by himself for a few minutes.

Let's look at the aspects of the very first day when you start swaddling and introducing rhythm and uniformity. These aspects are:

A. What is the best moment to start?
B. Putting your child to bed awake
C. Falling asleep
D. How long your baby should sleep
E. The relationship between feeding and sleeping

A. Swaddling for the very first time — what is the best moment?

For both methods, there are three options for the best moment to put your baby to sleep according to the new routine.

1. At night

If your child only sleeps well at night, you can start swaddling just before nightfall, immediately after feeding, and put your baby to bed while he is still awake. Being used to sleeping well at night, your child might just fall asleep in swaddling without rebelling. This positive experience might make it easier for your child to accept the swaddling without protesting too much the next day.

2. Immediately after the morning feed

Some children sleep through the night, wake up for a feed, go right back to sleep, wake up again and don't sleep at all during the rest of the day, becoming increasingly restless and fussy. In this case, you could start swaddling — and, if possible, putting your baby to bed awake — immediately after the first feed of the day. Again, your baby might accept the swaddling more easily because he is used to sleeping spontaneously at this time. As for yourself, you have the whole day ahead of you, and having slept well, you will feel stronger at this time. You will be better able to resist his crying and stick to your decision to introduce changes. You will also be better able to monitor your child's reactions and changing expression. After one good bout of sleep, he may look much more relaxed.

3. Immediately after a feed

When there is no rhythm nor good sleeping period at all, you can start after any feed. Do try to put your child to bed while he is still awake, however. When he cries in his bed, you can at least be sure that he is not hungry. You can also assume that he is tired, since he has hardly slept. Don't try to let your child play by himself after feeding this first time. If he cries at all, it is a healthy protest against the unfamiliar treatment. Decide for yourself which moment of the day is the best for you to start swaddling.

4. SWADDLE BEFORE A FEED AND PUT TO BED

Some newborns, and even older babies who drink very restlessly, can be swaddled before a feed for the first time. Being wrapped up tightly, they lie still and drink better and more quickly. Satisfied and less tired and tense, they fall asleep more easily. Again, when you put your child to sleep you know for a fact that your child has a full stomach because he drank more effectively. In some cases, exhausted infants can even be spared the first experiences of crying themselves to sleep.

> 'The district nurse advised me to swaddle him and showed me how to do it. Johnny calmed down visibly and stopped crying. At first I thought: that's a coincidence, I don't believe it. I must say I felt a bit sorry for him, lying there all wrapped up like a package, but I was so tired that I decided to do it at home that night. And what do you know, he slept for four hours and as of that day he didn't wake up more than once a night.'

B. Putting your child to bed awake

Many children don't know their bed as the place where they are supposed to fall asleep, and so don't like it. Creating a new habit is the only way you can make bed a favourite place. Relinquishing an old habit usually hurts, and this goes for both you and the child. Still, this short-lived pain (having to stand the cries of your baby without doing anything, and having to cry in your baby's case) is nothing compared with the huge achievement of his ability to fall asleep in his own bed. Once your child is able to fall asleep without help, he will gradually sleep for longer periods and wake up happy. His bed will then have become a familiar place in which he falls asleep, sleeps and wakes up again.

What can you expect the first time you put your child to bed awake?

RESISTANCE

The older the child and the longer the problem exists, the more resistance you can expect for the first few times or days. An exhausted five-week-old has little strength to protest fiercely. He may even fall asleep while you swaddle him, and wake up smiling three hours later. You may get some protests when you swaddle the second or third time, but there is a possibility that you will get no resistance at all. If the problem exists for five months, however, the reaction patterns between you and your child will have become more firmly established. Your child will offer more resistance when you begin to act differently. If he is used to falling asleep in your arms, for example, he will not accept being put to bed while he is still awake. He will protest furiously, supported by more physical strength. Don't let this scare you — his cries are just a healthy sign of anger.

A child who is used to crying for hours on end will be able to keep it up even when swaddled. Much depends on your baby's temperament, of course. Many children show similar behaviour, and still there are numerous small variations. This is only logical, because every child is unique and the duration and nature of the problem may differ. In addition, there is a variety of reaction patterns between parent and child.

SWEATING

A crying swaddled child can sweat a lot. What is acceptable? The child can get rid of excessive heat through his head, which is not swaddled. Once asleep, your child should sweat hardly or not at all, except on hot summer days. A sleeping child should not be flushed. If he is, and his feet and legs are cold, the warmth is distributed unevenly over the body. An extra blanket across his legs might solve the problem. Some children are literally hotheads, sweating all the time. Get to know your child and check his temperature a few times when he wakes up. A temperature up to about 37.6°C is normal.

CRYING

'How long should I let my baby cry in his bed without doing anything?' parents keep asking me. There is no universal answer to this. What's acceptable depends on the initial situation and what you can bear. Some children cry so much that parents tell me: 'His crying is in my head. Even when he doesn't cry, I hear him crying.' Five minutes appear like half an hour to many parents.

THE KITCHEN TIMER

As I indicated when I discussed the rules in Chapter 10, the kitchen timer can help as an objective entity. Set it for thirty minutes after you have put your baby to bed. I know from experience that babies usually cry less rather than more. Prepare yourself for his crying and have faith in your baby's strength. From a distance, support your child with love, no matter how difficult it is. Your child will sense it and will not feel abandoned. If you sit by his bed, he will remain too close to you, which makes it more difficult for him to let go and fall asleep. Place the bed so that you can peek in once in a while without being seen by your child.

Remember, going to his bed without picking him up is still giving him attention. Many parents tell me that their child is not helped when they show themselves. On the contrary, they find that their child cries even louder when they leave again. If your child is given latitude for a healthy protest, he can deploy his own strengths to learn and solve little problems by himself.

WHAT IS HALF AN HOUR OF CRYING LIKE?

Your baby's crying often sounds impressive — he's crying his heart out. If you listen carefully, however, you will find that after ten to fifteen minutes he begins to pause for breath. Half a minute of silence should also be considered as a breather. Let this be a comfort to you. It means that your child is not as upset as it seems. Start counting again when your baby pauses for breath, and disregard the time he has already cried. This means that you can reset the kitchen timer for another thirty minutes. Usually, children don't cry for more than thirty to sixty minutes, including pauses. And finally your child may suddenly fall asleep for two to three hours. Hooray! His initially red and perhaps even sweaty face will regain its regular complexion because he relaxes. He will probably cry less and less violently before his next sleep.

Resetting the kitchen timer after he first pauses for breath could be considered some kind of trick. It is. Still, it is a very useful trick, and a great support too. The worst part is over after fifteen minutes of heart-wrenching cries. Resetting the timer for another thirty minutes, you give your child a little more time to fall asleep on his own. Once the crying begins to subside, it is more acceptable for both parties. Parents often tell me that they let their child cry for more than an hour, because they feel that if they were to pick him up after such a long time, he would have worked so hard for nothing.

You will gradually learn to recognize the way your baby cries. You will be able to distinguish his cries of trying to fall asleep from his cries of hunger, boredom or pain. Once again, there is no special prescription for dealing with a crying baby. I can't tell you when you should eventually pick up your baby after all, give him a pacifier, or do anything else. The way to act depends on your own personality too. A breastfed three-week-old baby could respond well to a smooth transition of a small sip on the breast to be put to bed drowsy and satisfied. Make sure he doesn't begin to depend on it, though. Try to stop as soon as he accepts the swaddling. When you believe it is necessary to do something, do it lovingly, quietly and as neutrally as possible. Your child will become used to less and less attention when he has to fall asleep. The more he has to do it by himself, the sooner (often within a few days) he will accept the new situation.

> 'The first two days of swaddling, our ten-week-old daughter cried for twenty, fifteen, ten, and between one and five minutes before she fell asleep. Her resistance decreased. After one week she once cried for a whole hour (with pauses). We let her cry, which was sheer hell, and she fell asleep on her own. Since then she whines for one minute before she falls asleep, and we are so happy! She now sleeps for fourteen instead of eight hours, and she only cries when she is hungry or tired, while she used to cry for about four hours a day. We feel as if we've had a new baby.'

WHAT SHOULD I DO IF MY CHILD CRIES FOR LONGER?
Check if there is an obvious cause for the crying:

1. Are the sheet and blanket big enough, and are they tucked in far enough?

2. Are the swaddling cloths tight enough? Are the arms properly outstretched alongside the body, or is one of them sticking out? If necessary, re-swaddle your child.
3. Have you really given your child the chance to fall asleep by himself? Did he really not see you for half an hour? Or did you show your face and did you comfort him or touch him? If so, he expects to be picked up as he may be used to, and will cry more loudly to get his way. Did your child really cry without interruption or did you miss the breathers?

If you did indeed give your child enough time to fall asleep on his own, you have to break through the endless crying, for both your child and yourself. It can be very hard to have to listen to this long first session of crying. Especially when before you decided on this new approach, you tried to prevent all crying and comforted your child as much as possible.

Pick up your (swaddled) child and feed him in his bedroom (swaddling and all). If you use formula, dilute it with more water than usual in order to avoid overfeeding your child, while still giving him a sense of satisfaction. Then put your child to bed. He may fall asleep while he feeds. You could argue that his crying is rewarded with a feed. For a child who is not used to crying for such a long time, it isn't. Feeding relaxes your child, and a swaddled child cannot move because of the cloths. His fatigue will probably be stronger than the impulse to protest again. In these situations I have found that most children cry much less the second time and fall asleep by themselves. (For more information read section E, p. 156.)

C. Falling asleep
'His eyes become dull and empty.'

Sometimes, just before a baby falls asleep, his eyes become 'dull and empty,' many parents tell me. This scares them into thinking that the tight cloths have broken their child's will. They sometimes want to remove the cloths as soon as they see this. I know just what they mean, because I have often seen this when demonstrating the procedure of swaddling. Unlike the parents, seeing this fills me with gratitude and wonder, because I know that within seconds this phenomenon will be followed by sleep. What a wonderful idea that two simple cloths can achieve this change in no time at all — the change from restless and frustrated eyes to a peacefully sleeping baby!

Such a gift allows me to explain to parents the meaning of the child's body language, as a direct reaction to swaddling. What happens at such a moment is not that the child's will is broken by the parent's strong arm. On the contrary, helped by the pressure of the cloths, the child finally becomes aware of the limits of his own body. It must feel like coming home after being lost. In this safe haven he can let go and surrender to sleep. The fact that the eyes seem dull and empty means that the child withdraws into himself and shuts himself off to external stimulation.

And then ... 'Our child sleeps! He looks so horribly pale!'

This is another thing parents say just after their baby falls asleep. They worry and wonder whether this is normal. And let me assure you that it is. The contrast with the crying red face is huge. The pallor means that your child is very tired and deeply relaxed. Some parents have never seen this pale complexion before, because they only know their child in an 'over-active' state. The activity makes him a bright pink, even though he may have blue circles under his eyes. One parent told me: 'I don't know my child asleep. If he ever does sleep, I tiptoe through my own house, scared silly that I might wake him up.'

Your child's complexion is a part of his body language too. It allows you to tell how he is feeling. Therefore, don't miss the huge change you will experience when he catches up on sleep! Relatives and friends sometimes notice this sooner than you do, because they don't see your child all day and every day.

D. How long should your baby sleep?

SLEEPING TOO LONG

When you let your child sleep the first day you swaddle him, you have no idea what will happen. If your child develops a pattern of sleeping for six hours during the day, which is not unthinkable, he will want more night feeds. As a rule of thumb for children younger than six months, stick to four hours between feeds, counting from the start of one feed to the next. This applies only to the daytime, until the evening feed at approximately 10 pm. At night you can let your child sleep until he wakes up spontaneously. He could be so tired that he is hardly awake at all between feeds. If this is the case, skip the entertainment and the playpen, and put him to bed straight after nursing. You could think this goes against the rules of uniformity. True, but you should not keep an exhausted child awake just to conform to uniformity. A worn-out child is unable to learn from the situation. For uniformity you should focus on putting your child to bed awake as soon as he shows signs of weariness.

WAKING UP TOO SOON

Some children have no trouble falling asleep when they are swaddled, but wake up quickly, as they were used to. They are still stuck in the habit of short naps and have retained a certain degree of alertness in their sleep, which causes them to wake up too soon even when they are swaddled. This doesn't necessarily mean that they have had enough sleep. One mother told me: 'As I picked my child up because he woke up, and started to remove the swaddles, he promptly fell asleep again in my hands.'

If your child whimpers, or cries in fits and starts, just leave him. You can go and check without him seeing you, but don't pick him up. This will require some self-control, because you are probably used to responding to his every cry. Try not to relapse into this routine!

The old pattern of short naps can be difficult to break. Chances are that your child will gradually achieve deeper sleep. The cloths and the tightly tucked-in sheet and blanket (when it's hot, only the blanket) keep him from thrashing around. It is possible that he may complete his sleeping period alternating between short cries or whimpers and short naps. Don't underestimate the fact that he stays in bed much longer — it should be considered as enormous progress.

> 'In the beginning, our nine-week-old son cried for about ten minutes when I walked out after putting him to bed in swaddling. He then fell asleep for an hour, cried for another ten minutes, and then slept for another two hours.'

WHAT TO DO WHEN WHIMPERING DEVELOPS INTO REAL CRYING

When the crying doesn't seem to end, you can try to reassure your child. Put your hand over his eyes, making it dark. Firmly stroke his body and leave your hands on his back for a while. Don't pick him up. Check that his arms are still in place. Whisper or hum softly, but ensure that the room is quiet otherwise. In this way you don't add any other stimuli and allow your child to reach deeper sleep again. If this doesn't help, give him a pacifier (dummy) or nurse him for just a minute — in the bedroom. If you breastfeed, give him the breast you last ended with. These ways to comfort your child should be used during the first days of the new routine only, and should not become a new habit.

If the crying still doesn't stop, remove the swaddling and pick up the rhythm and uniformity of rule C: feeding, playing in your arms, playing alone in the playpen and as soon as you see the first signs of weariness, swaddling and putting your baby to bed. *This means that you don't need to stick to the thirty-minute-crying rule when your baby wakes up too soon.* This situation differs fundamentally from your baby not falling asleep after the first signs of becoming tired. His nap has given him enough energy to want to be awake again. Letting him cry won't work and is not appropriate for the situation. He will be justifiably angry for not being picked up, and will only cry more. It is best to offer him something from daytime life, though he will probably be unable to stay awake for very long. In this situation, therefore, you should consider feeding at the moment of giving him your attention, if possible followed by a brief moment in the playpen, swaddling upon the first signs of weariness, and bed. Don't be surprised if your child is tired immediately after feeding — after all, he only took a nap. In that case, skip playing alone, swaddle him and put him to sleep.

Picking your child up after it wakes up means:
  'I want to be fed now.'

Picking your child up when it gets tired means:
  'I can now go to sleep.'

Don't develop another unwanted pattern

Within a few days to a week after you started, your child will sleep longer, possibly for as much as two or three hours.

Don't allow the above-mentioned tips, concerning what to do when whimpering develops into real crying, to become a new behavioural pattern. The sleep cycle involves fluctuations between deep and light sleep. In a moment of light sleep, your child will be vaguely aware of the pacifier (dummy) or your stroking hand, if they come along regularly. He may become used to them and wake up to claim them. These are, of course, subconscious processes. Listen carefully to the exact sounds of your child's whimpering and crying when he continues to wake up too soon. Many parents tell me that their child is definitely less upset than before. Crying begins to sound like grumbling, there are regular pauses, and the child even falls asleep on and off. As I said before, don't get your child out of bed. Just leave him in his cot until it is really time to wake up. He can either sleep or whimper in the meantime. This allows him to get used to being in bed by himself for several hours. Without new stimuli, he will gradually sleep longer.

E. The relationship between feeding and sleeping

More feeds in the first few days

If you stick to the regular order of feeding after waking up, you may end up with a few more feeds per day. Make a note of how much and how often your child drinks. An extra bottle on the first day is never a problem. If you child appears to need even more than that, you can do the following. Take the number of prescribed scoops of milk powder for two bottles, and take the amount of water required for three.

This gives you three bottles of diluted formula. In this way, your child gets more fluid but just the prescribed amount of feed. This is a good way to give your child what he needs without giving too much. Besides, he probably won't even finish them all and may even reject them if there is little time in between. If so, just put your baby in the playpen without feeding him, and put him to bed upon the first signs of weariness.

SHORT NAPS: SWADDLE FOR SEVERAL FEEDS

Some children can't seem to get used to the new routine. Even when swaddled they have trouble falling asleep and sleeping. They are stuck in their over-active state and cry a lot. Even when asleep they are tense, making lots of jerky movements, though smaller because the swaddles and the tightly tucked in blankets don't offer much room for movement. Every sound causes another startle reflex. These children need more help to 'go under.' This is how it might work.

Start on the first day. If your child stays restless, give him another feed while swaddled, at least two hours after the start of the previous feed. Adding up the various steps, this makes for about two hours: a feed takes about thirty minutes, then your baby cries himself to sleep with intervals, which takes about forty-five minutes to an hour, a nap takes fifteen to thirty minutes, including one attempt to comfort him. Don't let your child get too upset. When his whimpering develops into real crying, pick him up, feed him swaddled and put him right back to bed. After this quiet feed he might prolong his nap. If he wakes up too soon again, repeat the quiet feed. Change him — only if it is really necessary — before feeding and swaddle him again immediately. Your child might achieve deep relaxation now that there are no more stimuli — external influences and self-stimulation caused by his own movements. If so, he can hopefully reach deep sleep.

In this way, your swaddled child spends half the day asleep. It can't do any harm to do this once, provided that the legs of a child younger than six months have enough room to spread when pulled up. Nor does it harm your baby's motor skills development.

After a few days your child may still wake up too quickly, but without crying. Leave him, do nothing. Without stimuli he just might fall asleep again, perhaps even for two hours. Try to remember this, and avoid a new routine of feeding every two hours. That could become a habit too!

When the worst fatigue is over, it is essential that you introduce rhythm and uniformity after all.

Let me repeat the routine for you:

Sleeping — waking up, then removing the cloths — changing and feeding, which can be considered as spending time together, playing together (implicit attention) — spending time alone / playing in the play-pen — tired, then swaddling and putting to bed awake

---

Once your child manages to sleep longer, another problem might occur. Your child, who hardly slept before, is now hardly awake any more. You might begin to have doubts when your child starts to whine after only a few minutes in the playpen. It will seem unlikely that your child is already tired again, because he has been up for such a short time. After all, he used to be awake for hours! Even though your child used to sleep many hours less, always consider his whining as a signal of weariness instead of boredom. And a signal of weariness means: 'I want to go to bed.' Act upon it. Experience has taught me that exhausted children catch up on lots of sleep once they manage to give in to it. And they have so much sleep to catch up on. They can sometimes sleep for two whole days, not counting the feeds.

THE FIRST WEEK: THIRD-DAY DIP

The first few days of swaddling, your child may sleep excessively. This gives him enough strength to offer resistance on the third day. Parents tell me this so often that I have come to consider this third-day dip as systematic.

The dip is caused by the baby's renewed resistance against swaddling and his relapse into the old sleeping pattern. Your rested child appears to become 'aware' of the fact that life is really quite different from before, and this confuses him. Or perhaps he doesn't want to give up his old habits too easily. He has enough energy to resist, since he is more rested than ever! He wakes up after a short nap during the day, and several times at night too, which he may not have done on previous nights. Ignore his whimpering completely and leave him in bed as long as you can manage (for about three hours from the start of the previous feed). Don't follow him into renewed restlessness. Stay firm and continue swaddling. He will probably overcome this dip within a day and stop resisting when he sees that he has no choice. Only then will he really relax and get the amount of sleep he needs. Should you stop the intervention because you feel sorry for him, your problems will start all over again.

If you use the method without swaddling, your child may need a few extra days to get used to the new routine. The dip will then occur on the fifth day or thereabouts.

The new routine has become a habit

Once you and your child have become used to swaddling and the new routine, a recurring pattern will set in. Some children continue to need to cry for five to ten minutes before they fall asleep. Other children smile as soon as they see the cloths, still others continue to protest when they are placed on the cloths, until they feel the pressure of the cloth on their arm. Recognition of the cloths, whether they see them or feel them, causes them to relax and surrender to swaddling. Most children develop a reasonably stable sleeping and waking rhythm after one week of consistent swaddling. In the first five months of their life, children who are used to rhythm can sleep for about two hours after every feed, or a bit longer after the morning feed and a bit less in the afternoon. Specific schedules differ — they are all fine as long as they show rhythm. Children with a regular pattern cry considerably less. You will no longer need to entertain your baby for twenty-four hours a day, and have some time to yourself every once in a while! In addition, your baby will be much happier.

The second phase: the new pattern sinks in

After one to two weeks both parents and baby are accustomed to the new routine. This does not mean that the child will adhere to it on his own. He still needs to rely on his parents and the swaddling cloths for some time. In order to allow the newly acquired rhythm and uniformity to really sink in, you have to continue for at least six more weeks.

Start counting when your child accepts the swaddling cloths (even if he still cries a little before falling asleep) and shows an individual sleeping and waking rhythm that really suits him. You will know that this is the case when he enjoys cuddling, loves playing by himself, is able to fall asleep, and wakes up rested. In most cases this is after one to two weeks, but it may take a little longer because you hate to hear your child cry and opt for a milder approach, for instance, or because you don't swaddle consistently. Some parents swaddle only during the night in the first few weeks, only to discover that their child needs it during the day as well. In such situations, several weeks may pass before you can start the second-phase countdown.

Renewed restlessness

Your baby could get restless again in the course of this second phase. One of the reasons could be that the swaddling is not tight enough and/or has become too small. While it was fine at the start, the swaddling is now inappropriate for the older, and therefore stronger, child. He needs more pressure from the cloths to match his increased physical strength. If this is indeed the cause of your baby's restlessness, it is very easy to eliminate it and things will calm down instantly. Don't forget to check that the blanket is big enough to be tucked in properly.

Loose swaddling

> 'If the swaddles were even the tiniest bit looser than usual, Arno didn't stop crying until I wrapped him all over again into a tight little package. I could just see his face relaxing.'

A small survey among one hundred parents, whose babies I helped, shows that babies need swaddling for an average of three months.

Once routine and independence have become a part of your child, he will be able to stick to them without the help of the swaddling cloths, although he continues to need *you* for the rhythm and uniformity.

Some children need to cry for variable amounts of time before they fall asleep, even though the introduction of routine is a success.

> 'We have now been underway for seven weeks and our ten-week-old son still cries loudly for fifteen to thirty minutes before he sleeps for three hours on end. At night he falls asleep at once without even protesting, and sleeps through the night except for one feed.'

The third phase: reduction in swaddling — how to stop

If it took your child one or two weeks to break the old pattern and develop a new and steady rhythm, you can try to start reducing the swaddling after another six weeks. This means you have started the regime seven to eight weeks ago. Some children make it clear that they have had enough.

You may notice the following signals:
1. Your child wakes up crying even though he slept well, while he used to chatter contentedly after waking up.
2. Your child suddenly wakes up early in the morning, begins to cry and won't go back to sleep. This may mean that he accepts the swaddling upon going to sleep but not upon waking up. He seems to want to move, which is impossible.

3. Your child begins to protest while you swaddle him,
   while he used to welcome the cloths. He also cries a lot
   before he allows sleep to take over.

Some children 'accidentally' demonstrate that they no
longer need the cloths.

For example, your child shows the ability to keep an
excellent rhythm and to sleep well during a period when
swaddling is not appropriate, such as a fever during an
illness, after a vaccination or during a heat wave in the
summer.

Both during, and after, cutting down, the tightly tucked-
in blanket remains indispensable for the familiar sense of
boundary. You need to tuck your child in every time he goes
to sleep (only in hot weather can you use only the sheet).
Make sure the blanket is wide enough to be tucked in well.
When you put your child to bed, try to place his arms alongside his body underneath the blanket. He may leave them
there because he is used to that posture. Stick to the same
ritual of going to bed as much as possible, even though the
swaddling is omitted. Don't change the place where you
change your baby before putting him to bed yet. Stroke his
arms and legs firmly, as if you are swaddling him. He will
continue to recognize bedtime. Another important aspect
of the reduction phase is to apply rhythm and uniformity
in your actions as strictly as you can, just like in the start-
up phase. Recognition will allow your child to surrender
to sleep more easily, even without the swaddling. Start the
reduction process on a quiet day.

There are several ways to cut down on swaddling. You
can stop abruptly or gradually, and you can leave out the
cloths altogether or one at a time. Your child will let you
know what's best for him.

Stopping abruptly

This means that as of a certain moment, you leave out the swaddling cloths altogether. Replace them with a fitted sleeping bag, allowing your baby to feel the familiar boundary on his tummy and at his feet. You can take in the sleeping bag, sewing it to fit your baby, and making it wider as he grows. Use an unpadded sleeping bag, with long sleeves if possible, to keep your baby's arms and hands warm, even when they end up on top of the blankets while he sleeps. The resistance of the fabric also allows less movement. From this perspective, a sleeping bag is a good alternative to the swaddling cloths. A child is never too old for a sleeping bag. Children generally love to feel boundaries. Children who are used to them even ask for them. A sleeping bag should always be long enough for the legs to be outstretched. Make sure it isn't too long for a younger child. The neckline should fit your baby's neck quite snugly. The sack should not be so big that your child can roll around in it and become entangled. A sleeping bag without sleeves should have nicely fitting armholes. Never put your child in a sleeping bag with his arms inside — he could easily become entangled in it, and if he should end up on his tummy, he wouldn't have his arms to help him turn back or, if necessary, push off and away.

Gradual reduction

It is best to start leaving off the swaddling cloths during one of his best sleeps. This could be the night, because your child sleeps deeper then. Replace the cloths with the fitted sleeping bag described above. Or you may prefer to start after the first feed, because your child always falls asleep immediately after this feed and prolongs the night. Lots of children do this. If your child sleeps well without swaddling, you can try putting him to bed without swaddling more often the next day. You could continue to swaddle him in the late afternoon or the evening — he may be a bit fussy then. It might work to only swaddle him at those times. You are not being uniform, but it often works because swaddling is familiar to your child.

Without the definition of the firmly wrapped cloths

Start by leaving one arm free when you swaddle. Dress your child in a long-sleeved sleepsuit (footie), ensuring that his free arm stays warm too and he still feels some sort of definition. The transition is less sudden then. In hot weather, leave off the bodysuit rather than the long-sleeved sleepsuit (footie). If the free arm doesn't cause a relapse into restlessness, you can leave the second arm free after a few days. This means that the big cloth can go and you can continue with the leg cloth. For a child younger than six months, leave enough room for him to pull up his legs and spread them. For a child older than six months, pull the cloth tightly across the entire leg. You need several safety pins and should always close the cloth below the feet. Keep your child comfortably warm again — just like he is used to with the two cloths — but not too warm. You could dress him in a pair of pyjamas or a sweater. Depending on the room or outside temperature you can give him one or two layers of clothing. Make sure the sleeves end on his hand, preferably with a neatly fitting border, and make sure the neckline also fits snugly. If your child continues to sleep well with both arms free, you can leave out the leg cloth as well. Replace it with a fitted sleeping bag. Continue to tuck your child in tightly with both the sheet and the blanket.

HOW WILL YOU KNOW IF IT IS TOO SOON TO STOP?

You will know that your child still needs swaddling when he relapses into the old pattern of crying a lot, having trouble falling asleep, and sleeping less. If this happens, immediately start the swaddling in combination with the predictable routine again. It is not a good idea to allow the renewed restlessness to continue for several days. You may end up in a downward spiral, and unwanted habits might creep in, such as giving your child a pacifier (dummy) more often, or picking him up more often when he cries. You will do this with the best intentions of course, because after all, it is very strange for your child to be without swaddles. Before you know it, he depends on you again, and that would be such a shame for both of you. Or perhaps you want to give your child a few days to get used to sleeping without swaddles. You might decide to stick to the predictable rhythm and uniformity and falling asleep on his own, not generating any new habits. I know from experience that this simply doesn't work in the case of a relapse, and results in a downward spiral of restlessness.

Another possibility is that your child doesn't have a major relapse but has more trouble falling asleep and wakes up sooner. In that case you could try to hang on for one day. Allow your child to cry again in order to fall asleep — it may be temporary. If necessary, go and check on him without him seeing you. If he wakes up too soon and begins to whine, simply leave him until it is time for his feed. Your child may need to get used to the new approach. If things take a turn for the worse, and your child becomes fatigued again, it is definitely too soon to stop swaddling. Pick up where you left off.

Try to stop again after another two weeks. For all you know it may work the next time. If the attempt fails again and your child is around seven months old, seek the advice of your health centre.

Reduce at six months

In view of an increasing ability to roll over on his tummy, it is wise to start reducing swaddling when your child is six months old. Phase Two of the swaddling process, the six weeks of letting the new routine sink in, must have passed, of course. If you have started at a very young age, you can start reducing sooner. Watch your child if he is over six months.

Older than six months? Then check that:

✿ his feet don't stick out of the cloths
✿ the cloths are tight enough around the legs
✿ no arms can be wriggled out
✿ the blanket is big enough
✿ the blanket is tucked in high enough and far enough
✿ the mattress fits and the tucked-in blanket stays
   firmly in place between mattress and bed

If your swaddled child is able to roll over on his tummy, *stop* swaddling!

When can a relapse occur?

Growing up involves all kinds of developmental phases which may cause a relapse. The skills of raising the upper body, standing up and walking are acquired gradually, just like the development of consciousness. But despite the gradual nature of these developments, unexpected and abrupt changes (of consciousness) can sometimes be observed. The consciousness reaches farther into the outer world, but also into the inner world. Children become increasingly aware of themselves, as I described in the chapter about the phases of development of the young child. That is why I will only briefly mention the issue here. Such a new developmental phase may cause sleeping problems. A child who has just learned to stand up enjoys standing up in bed, too. Your one-year-old has discovered how he can have his way. He manages to call you back three times after the usual bedtime ritual — it may mark the start of renewed sleeping problems. Or, your coughing child has needed you for several nights in a row. Now that he is better, he begins to claim the attention he doesn't need any more. He wants to retain his newly acquired rights.

Sometimes it is not clear why your child gets restless again. Maybe you have been too indulgent without realizing it, and you have let the routine slip a bit. Sometimes parents need a not-so-strict rhythm. It is healthy to slacken the reins a little, after a while. Parents feel they can breathe again. But how much freedom should be given?

Common sense and your child's reactions should be your guide. Predictability should be the basis of everything.

Which children risk having a relapse?

❁ Children who are very open and who suck up influences like a sponge. These are the children who are thrown off balance as soon as things happen outside the daily routine.

❁ Children who always want more than they can handle. Parents who have such a child will instantly know what I mean. It may be apparent from the moment they see the light of day. It is as if their tiny body just doesn't fit. These are the children who are frustrated over any little thing until they can control their own body. Once they are able to move through the house, they are visibly happier.

Both groups of children respond well to rhythm and uniformity, both with and without swaddling. Every bit of rest these children get is a bonus, even with the occasional relapse after stopping. Don't let a relapse disappoint you. The predictability of the day, rhythm and uniformity are extra important for these children.

What to do in case of a relapse

Look at your current situation with a critical eye and some distance. Is the life of your child still marked by rhythm and uniformity? Are there any loopholes that your growing and clever child manages to find without fail? If so, I advise you to start re-introducing rhythm and uniformity very strictly during one week, without swaddling. Allow your child to cry out of protest, and give him a properly fitting sleeping bag and tucked-in blanket, should these be lacking.

> 'When my child cries or is restless and has trouble falling asleep, these days, I hold him tightly. Especially his arms. Experiencing a feeling similar to swaddling calms him down.'

Clarity in an educational sense is now of the utmost importance. Put your words into actions. Send the message as you speak it — your child perfectly understands your body language. Let any comforting during the night be brief, loving but businesslike, in order to renounce any unwanted habits and to prevent new ones from creeping in. If it is at all possible, don't take the child to your own bedroom.

If this doesn't work, you might consider a brief period of swaddling again, but no longer than necessary. A few days or even just once could be enough to turn the tide and make your baby relax again.

The swaddling cloths can sometimes be convenient, for example when your child can't fall asleep because of a very busy day or strange environment. Swaddling can be just what he needs to fall asleep, just this once.

You need to know for sure that your child is not whining because he is getting sick. Sick children can develop a high fever in a short time. When in doubt, don't swaddle. Make sure also that your child's cot or bed meets the safety requirements described in Chapter 12 (pp. 136–140). The swaddling method and the cloths should be appropriate for your child's age.

Remember that as soon as you see your child attempting to roll over on his tummy, you should stop swaddling!

14. Questions and answers

*How many days can I expect my baby to cry
before falling asleep?*

After two days you should notice a considerable change,
provided that:

* you have adhered consistently to the rules of the
  game with regard to rhythm and uniformity
* you have made the bed and put your baby to sleep
  as instructed
* you really have not shown yourself while your baby
  cried himself to sleep

The change can be recognized from the following signals:

* the duration and intensity of crying begin to
  decrease
* your baby is clearly more satisfied to play/be by
  himself
* your baby feeds better

Continue the method when you notice these improvements,
no matter how small they may seem. In some cases, the real
breakthrough may take as long as five to seven days.

If you notice no improvement at all *after two days, don't
continue in the same way.* Adopt a middle course.

A FEW SUGGESTIONS:

1. Try giving your child a pacifier (dummy) after fifteen
   minutes of crying, instead of half an hour. Perhaps he
   needs a shorter cry to fall asleep and crying longer only
   upsets him more. Given at just the right moment, for

instance after about fifteen minutes, the pacifier (dummy) may just be the support he needs to let go completely.

2. Help your child by sitting next to the bed with loving but silent attention, and holding the pacifier (dummy) until he falls asleep. Give him no other form of attention whatsoever. In this way you set an intermediate goal for yourself — teaching your child to be in his own bed for longer without external stimuli.

IF YOU DON'T SWADDLE YOUR CHILD: ADD SWADDLING TO RHYTHM AND UNIFORMITY

If the above doesn't help at all, add swaddling to your method, unless there are reasons not to do so. Do it consistently throughout the day whenever you put your baby to sleep. Your baby must get used to a new routine.

IF YOU DO SWADDLE YOUR CHILD

Take your swaddled child in your arms or put him in the pram and walk around until he sleeps (don't put him in a sling, because that is too hot). As soon as your child is in a deep sleep, put him in his bed. There is little chance that he will wake up, because the transition from your arm to the bed is less obvious with the swaddling cloths. It is likely, however, that he will need more time to learn how to fall asleep by himself.

STOP SWADDLING

If nothing of the above helps, it might be better to stop swaddling. I can't give you any specific advice on this, but I do have some ideas. Your child may have fallen behind even more because he cried even more than before, because he had to cry himself to sleep. Or he may have slept less because the rules specified that you couldn't let him sleep in your arms any more.

Try to help him sleep in other ways. Perhaps you can give him the required predictable regularity after all, even if you help and comfort him more than I advised. After all, predictability is a great help to any child in any situation.

What do I do when both methods fail?

Visit a medical professional to have your child thoroughly examined. If necessary, you will be referred to a specialist. I assume, however, that any medical causes have been ruled out before, because most babies are examined regularly. Earlier, I advised you to visit your health centre before starting the method. Nevertheless, there could be a medical problem now.

Take a critical look at the way your baby cries and becomes quiet at intervals. I wouldn't worry about a child who cries his eyes out while is alone in his bed but goes quiet almost as soon as he is picked up. If he is happy as long as he gets attention, a medical cause is unlikely. If your child starts to cry his eyes out for no apparent reason at all, whether he is alone or with you, and stops crying for no apparent reason too, though, an allergy could be the cause of his (and your) misery.

Can the breastfeeding mother's diet be the cause of a failing method?

In very rare cases, an allergy is overlooked. I know of one mother whose baby had even been hospitalized and who had been on a hypoallergenic diet for four weeks, supervised by a dietician, and still the baby's allergy wasn't found. Allergies are hard to diagnose.

Blood tests are often unreliable with young children, even though they are done.

As a breastfeeding mother you can do as follows: express your milk for four days in order to keep up the production. During these days, give your child the strictest hypoallergenic bottle-feeding — there is quite a variety available. This allows you to test whether any substance in your diet ending up in your breast milk is the cause of your baby's crying. If he shows significantly different behaviour during these four days, this is definitely the case. I advise you to seek the advice of the health centre or to find others who can help you determine which substance is the cause of his misery. If you manage to trace the substance, you can adjust your own diet and continue breastfeeding.

Can bottle-feeding be the cause of a failing method?

If you bottle-feed your child it could also be worthwhile switching to hypoallergenic feeding for at least one to two weeks, if you haven't tried this before. Your child could even be on a hypoallergenic formula which is inappropriate for him. Seek guidance from the health centre.

What do I do when my child does manage to fall asleep but wakes up too soon all the time?

1. Reread the section 'Waking up too soon' (p. 153).

2. Your child may still be over-stimulated because he stays awake for too long and becomes exhausted.

Try to answer the following questions for yourself, in
order to determine whether or not this is the cause of
his waking up so soon:

* Does it take you long to change and feed him?
* Do you spend much time playing together and giving him attention?
* Does he then have enough energy left to amuse himself for a while?

Some children are very eager and curious. Even when they
are tired they will welcome some time in the playpen, because
their attention is drawn by new things. They possibly even
play for too long, because they remain 'enchanted' by some
mechanical toy, such as a musical mobile. Have you sewn little bells on his socks, or is he wearing a rattling bracelet?
   What can you do?

* Replace the time of playing together with the
  'implicit attention' I described earlier, which hardly
  takes up any time at all.
* Reduce the number of stimuli. Give him simple toys
  appropriate for his age. He will indicate at the right
  time when he is tired and needs to go to bed again.
  More relaxed and less stressed, he will gradually
  sleep longer.

3. This amount of sleep may simply be enough for your child.
   This is the case when your child:

* wakes up happy
* is able to play by himself contentedly within the routine of daily events until it is time to go to sleep again
* is able to fall asleep by himself

Should I continue to feed every two hours when he continues to wake up too early?

If short naps are indeed enough for your child, don't continue feeding him every two hours. Change the sequence of events, but be consistent in this new order.

The order now becomes as follows:

1. Sleeping — waking up — removing the cloths (if you swaddle)
2. Playing together briefly/cuddling when changing
3. Playing by himself in the playpen
4. Feeding by schedule or upon the clear indication of your child
5. Playing by himself in the playpen again
6. Swaddling upon the first signs of weariness (if you swaddle) and putting him to bed awake.

If your child falls asleep while you feed him, this means that he has played by himself for too long (point 3). You may need some time to find a good balance.

For how long must I follow the 'rigid' regularity routine? When can I go shopping and visit friends again?

You can definitely loosen the reins a bit after about two weeks. But let yourself be guided by your baby's body language, and never let go of the two basic rules of uniformity — put your baby to bed awake (swaddled or not) upon the first signs of weariness, and feed him as soon as he wakes up. After the first two weeks, you can put him to sleep in the pram (swaddled or not) if you like, so that he can sleep while you take a walk. When you come home, you can just leave him in the pram until he wakes up. To avoid him getting too hot, throw back a blanket if necessary.

It will not always be possible to be guided by your child's rhythm. That's fine — a rested child has some reserve and will soon catch up on any lack of sleep. If you need to travel for several hours, it is best for your child (at least until the age of six months) to be fed upon arrival at your destination, regardless of his feeding time, and to be put to sleep shortly after. This won't be a problem if you use the swaddling cloths. He will know that he is now allowed to sleep and will let go.

Can I give him a pacifier (dummy) to help him fall asleep?

If he is used to having a pacifier (dummy) in bed, you can. If, however, you have to go to him repeatedly because he loses it, the process of learning to fall asleep by himself will be disturbed. In addition, going into his bedroom makes the letting-go process between you and your child harder. In such a situation, set a limit for yourself and go back for the pacifier only once, for instance. This creates clarity. The pacifier may become unnecessary or even be ultimately rejected by your child once he is more rested.

Research has shown that babies lose their pacifier after fifteen minutes, on average. I suspect that this is caused by the muscles in the mouth relaxing on the moment of falling asleep.

My swaddled baby can't suck his thumb. Now what?

A swaddled child can't suck his thumb. Well, he can't do it when he is upset or crying or jerking his arms either. Swaddling usually results in the same rest as sucking on a thumb does. 'I feel bad about swaddling my baby who wants to suck his thumb,' parents sometimes say. Or they say, 'My child can never learn to suck his thumb this way.'

Leaving one arm free when swaddling to allow the baby to suck his thumb usually has a contrary effect. The baby stays restless. To my great surprise I have seen babies find their thumb while they were by themselves in the playpen, after swaddling had yielded results.

Can swaddling cause the back of the head to become flattened?

Yes, it can, due to the face-up sleeping posture. It's not the swaddling that does it, though — it makes no difference whether you swaddle or not. The phenomenon is usually temporary.

What can you do to prevent it? If you breastfeed, your baby's head is alternately turned to the right and to the left. When you bottle-feed, do the same. Put your baby to bed on his back with his head turned slightly, again alternating between left and right.

Put your baby in the playpen on his tummy every now and then, watching over him from a small distance, or practise while you play together. Take your child in your arms on his side and encourage him, by talking or singing, to look up at you. You can also do this sitting on the floor and putting him on his tummy on your lower legs. When he turns his head, he uses his neck muscles. Physiotherapists tell me that the exercise of these muscles also helps shape the back of the head.

Isn't swaddling simply another word for using a straitjacket?

Many parents are alarmed by the idea of swaddling and associate it with the Middle Ages or a straitjacket. They find it difficult to watch me swaddle their child for the first time. They feel suffocated just by the sight of it, and I can imagine that — the baby's freely moving arms can't budge by the time I've finished. Any protest voiced that first time only makes it worse for them! Luckily, these feelings of anxiety are often followed by the relief of see-ing their child relax, let go and fall asleep. Accept your own resistance without letting it affect your motivation for swaddling. Once you have seen how your baby thrives on swaddling, your resistance will evaporate like snow in summer. Other people could give you a hard time, though, because after all, they can't see how much better your child is doing.

Swaddling has nothing to do with limitation of freedom. After all, a child is swaddled only at those times when it really wants to lie still and sleep. I even venture to say that the opposite is true: children who are subjected to the continuous, uncontrolled movements of their arms and legs have to endure a limitation of freedom. They don't have control over their limbs. Their limbs are moving them rather than the other way round.

Does swaddling affect motor skills development?

On the contrary: motor skills development is helped by periods in which the body's movements are more or less at a standstill. This is what happens when a child is put to sleep and actually does sleep, and the parent creates the conditions for a healthy balance of active play and rest. Many children find this balance naturally, but as we have seen, some children cannot control their movements — they are victims of their own body. Their movements are chaotic and unfocused, which could result in a stagnation of motor skills development. Forced rest due to swaddling and/or being tucked-in tightly in bed makes their movements visibly more focused during their waking hours. They are clearly more in control of their limbs.

Lying on his back while he sleeps, your child needs to be put on his tummy regularly when he is awake. You can start doing this as soon as your baby is born. It promotes healthy motor skills and sense of self.

Many a restless baby is carried around a lot by his parents, put in a bouncer or on the sofa, surrounded by pillows, though he is unable to keep his body upright or sit up by himself. Such a child will be happy for a while — after all, there is much more to be seen sitting up than lying down. The trick does not encourage him, however, to learn to roll over, sit up or crawl by himself. Being surrounded by pillows, he has no reason to do so.

I see so little of my child. When can I give him some attention?

If you were used to giving your child lots of attention, the transition to sleeping most of the day in his own bed can be quite a shock. You will find, though, that the contact between you and your child becomes more intense than before as you are both more rested and relaxed. Real contact was hardly possible at all through the haze of fatigue, even though you may not have noticed it. You shouldn't even try to give attention to a child who wants to sleep. What you can do, occasionally, is sit by his bed after he has fallen asleep, and enjoy him in silence while he sleeps.

Can I let my child sleep in a sling or pram?

Better not during the first two weeks of getting into the routine. Once your child has found a good rhythm and is able to fall asleep by himself, you can, for example, take one walk per day with the pram. If he falls asleep in the pram, it is best to leave him there until he wakes up on his own. This will hardly disturb his rhythm.

You can also carry him in the sling once a day, until he wakes up for a feed, without disturbing his rhythm. You should not swaddle him in a sling — that would be too hot.

Endnotes

1. Petra Weeda, *Puur Kind Babydagboek,* Weleda Nederland BV, Zoetermeer 2002

2. Ibid.

3. Alber Soesman, *De twaalf zintuigen. Poorten van de ziel,* Zeist 1998

4. A.M.L. Coenen, *De slaap,* Assen 1979

5. S. Bruijns en M. Buskop-Kobussen (ed.), *Diagnostiek en interventie voor verpleegkundigen in de Ouder- en Kindzorg,* Assen 1996

6. M. Weissbluth, 'Sleep-loss Stress and temperamental difficultness: Psychobiological processes and practical considerations' in *Temperament in childhood,* London 1989, pp. 357–375
   —, 'Sleep temperament interactions' in *Clinical and educational applications of temperament research,* Lisse 1989, pp. 113–116

7. Tracy Hogg and Melinda Blau, *Wat je baby vertelt,* Amsterdam 2001

Glossary

Bed

- ✿ always put your baby to sleep on his back
- ✿ cover your baby to just above the shoulders
- ✿ make the bed so that his feet reach the footboard
- ✿ use a big enough sheet and big enough woollen or cotton blanket
- ✿ tuck in the sheet and blanket tightly under the mattress
- ✿ no toys in bed, no mobile over the bed
- ✿ you can give him one cuddly toy and/or music box (wind up once only)
- ✿ use a level mattress fitting snugly in the crib or bed

First signs of weariness

- ✿ yawning
- ✿ pallor
- ✿ rubbing the eyes
- ✿ whining
- ✿ becoming more lively
- ✿ breaking off eye-contact and looking away

Over-stimulation, avoid

- ✿ television
- ✿ radio
- ✿ use of baby bouncer or first-stage car seat outside feeding times
- ✿ constant entertainment of your child
- ✿ mechanical toys
- ✿ baby-gym or similar contraption for children under three months (they aren't suitable for children under three months)

Pointers for the worst hours of crying
- ✿ carry him in a sling (not swaddled) or similar, between feeds
- ✿ take one walk per day with the pram (swaddled)

Reduce travelling

Maintain the rhythm by:
- ✿ putting your child to sleep when it's time, in his own bed at home or, during a trip, in the pram (swaddled) or sling (not swaddled)
- ✿ receiving visitors at home rather than going to them, particularly during the first two weeks of starting the method

Rhythm and uniformity during the day
- ✿ waking up (removing the swaddles), immediately followed by
- ✿ feeding, immediately followed by
- ✿ playing together: up to two months, implicit attention while changing and feeding

FROM TWO MONTHS UPWARDS:

- ✿ cuddling/making contact on your lap even after feeding
- ✿ playing by himself in a fixed place, preferably the playpen
- ✿ upon the first signs of weariness: (swaddling and) putting him to bed awake

Sleeping clothes with swaddling
- ✿ socks, make sure his feet stay warm
- ✿ bodysuit or bodysuit plus t-shirt
- ✿ in very hot weather, swaddle naked

Sleeping clothes without swaddling
- ✿ socks, make sure his feet stay warm
- ✿ snugly-fitted sleeping bag made of natural materials, no synthetic padding
- ✿ clothes should cover the neck and shoulders
- ✿ keep his hands warm, if necessary with two layers of long-sleeved shirts

Success
- ✿ willingness to 'go for it'
- ✿ a well-balanced decision to change makes you firm
- ✿ stick to rhythm and uniformity
- ✿ be and remain consistent
- ✿ accept crying as a way to let go when he learns to fall asleep on his own
- ✿ set the kitchen timer to thirty minutes for objective timing for crying himself to sleep

Times between feeds during the day, counting from the start of the previous feed
- ✿ at least two hours
- ✿ at most four hours

Uniform approach
- ✿ Handling your child with predictable rhythm and uniformity (plus swaddling)

Uniform places for everything
- ✿ always let your baby sleep in the same room in the same bed (could be a different place at night)
- ✿ always let your baby play alone in the same place, preferably in the playpen

Resources

Some of the nightwear and equipment mentioned in this book is relatively easy to find. Long-sleeved sleepsuits (footies) and bodysuits (babygrows), for example, are available from high-street retailers such as Mothercare.

Swaddling cloths and non-padded sleeping bags are harder to come by. In the UK, you could try:

— Blooming Marvellous
   (www.bloomingmarvellous.co.uk)
— Green Baby (www.greenbaby.co.uk)
— Perfectly Happy People
   (www.thebabycatalogue.com)

In the USA:
— Colic Shop
   (www.colicshop.com/swaddling-blankets.shtml)
— Kiddopotamus (www.kiddopotamus.com)
— Miracle Blanket (www.miracleblanket.com)
— Slumber Sounds
   (www.slumbersounds.com/swaddling-blanket-intro.htm)

In Australia:
— KiwiGreen (www.kiwigreen.com.au)
— Snug as a Bug (www.snugasabug.com.au)

Companies selling fairly-traded or organic babywear often advertise in natural or alternative parenting magazines such as Juno (www.junomagazine.com) and The Green Parent (www.thegreenparent.co.uk) in the UK. You could try:

— Greenfibres (www.greenfibres.com)
— People Tree (www.peopletree.co.uk)
— Baby Kind (www.babykind.co.uk)
— Born Direct (www.borndirect.co.uk)

Please note that these lists are not exhaustive and that the information may become out of date quickly. We apologize for any obvious omissions.